BY RONA JAFFE

The Best of Everything
Away from Home
The Last of the Wizards (*children's book*)
Mr. Right is Dead
The Cherry in the Martini

RONA JAFFE

*The Cherry
in the Martini*

SIMON AND SCHUSTER   NEW YORK

PUBLISHED BY SIMON AND SCHUSTER
ROCKEFELLER CENTER, 630 FIFTH AVENUE
NEW YORK, NEW YORK 10020

FIRST PRINTING

LIBRARY OF CONGRESS CATALOG CARD
NUMBER: 66-21819
DESIGNED BY EDITH FOWLER
MANUFACTURED IN THE UNITED STATES
OF AMERICA
BY THE BOOK PRESS INCORPORATED,
BRATTLEBORO, VERMONT

FOR MY REAL-LIFE PARENTS

FOREWORD

None of this may be the way it happened, but it's the way I remember it. I'm sure none of the people it happened to remember it right either, because people never do. Things are real because they seem that way. And so we live all our lives remembering it the way it seemed.

The Cherry
in the Martini

The following is an excerpt from a story I wrote when I was thirteen:

Once there was an old maid who worked in an office. Every night after work she ate dinner alone at Schrafft's.

Tonight she decided to be festive, so she ordered pheasant under glass. She looked around the warmly lit room at the romantic diners and noticed that she was the only person there who was alone.

She stared morosely at the cherry in the martini. . . .

1
A Case History

There must be such a thing as mental hypochondria as well as physical—when hearing of the symptoms of a certain aberration one immediately begins to feel them in himself—and so I hesitate to write this story. And yet, mental hypochondria is not my pleasure. I can immediately conjure up symptoms of ulcers, heart failure, anything you want to detail, but like most people I like to keep my mind special. If anyone else is eccentric, I certainly don't want to be. And yet . . .

It was the end of last summer, in the country, where the nights were cold and bright with stars, the days still swimming-pool days. We were in the dining room of my large old country house, six or eight of us, all good friends. There was a fire in the grate of the dining room, which hadn't seen a fire in twenty years. A fire in both the living room and the dining room! It was like an English novel, we all felt, since we had grown up in clean homes with artificial fireplaces and wax fruit and maids who washed ashtrays as soon as you used them, so you wondered if you had ever really been there at all. We were all in our late twenties and early thirties, which is important to what follows.

Looking around the warm, fire-lit room, at the friends who loved one another, at the wine—very dry, *vin du jour,* in delicate glasses meant for holidays (there were no other kind in that house)— one of my friends said, "This is the first time we have ever been all alone in a house with no grown-ups!"

No one said, "But we are grownups." No one said anything; we all smiled happily and agreed. A house with no grownups . . . is this what one waits for until one realizes with dismay that everyone else is very young and the "grownups" are old and haven't been frightening for years? What of the years between? Where have they gone? Where were we . . . or rather, who were we? Or is this all life is?

Then someone began talking about schizophrenic children. He had a relative who had a schizophrenic child—a child so good, so obedient, so anxious to please, that the parents had finally taken her to a doctor because it did not seem natural. And it turned out this was not natural. Then he began describing symptoms. I sat there, at first only interested, then disturbed. The behavior of the child . . . I don't remember my own behavior very well, only that all through my childhood my parents told me I was very bad, and then years later my mother told me she had always worried because I was so good. But the dream life! That held me. It was as if he were telling me, like some frightening mind reader, of the dream life I had had. "Some children grow out of it naturally at puberty," he said. "It seems to be a combination of a glandular change and a more social environment. The doctors now try to get the schizophrenic child to relate to other children, to have real-life friends instead of the friends of his imagination." But if no one tries. . . ?

For years, when my friends were reading *Nancy Drew and the Hidden Staircase,* I read psychology books. They were all over the house. My mother was a psychology major at college, my uncle a frustrated would-be doctor. No one but the school librarian told me what I must not read, and from the school library I simply stole the forbidden books. Words children do not understand are no problem. If the sentence makes sense, the words fall into place in some part of the mind that needs no words. I have been reading psychology books ever since, because to me, case histories are more interesting than the plot of any novel. So I think I am right. How strange that no one ever wrote about this, or perhaps, that no one remembers having been through it. I know that I had a special dream world as a child, that I grew out of it; and I remember it all as clearly as others remember playing baseball or dolls with their friends or fooling grownups or being in love.

I don't know why it began. There are always theories: loneliness, lack of love, lack of communication with parents. I only remember that there was a world I invented that was more real than the world I had to live in day by day, that I protected my secret world as silently and naturally as a nun says her prayers, and that it was the only world that mattered. I do not remember food, or smells, or going to new places, although I ate every-

thing I could and went to many places, including
the World's Fair, camp, and various towns where
my family rented summer houses. I remember few
books I read and very little of what I learned in
school, although I was an A student. To this day
I add on my fingers and often make mistakes.
I do not remember the day I discovered sex or
little boys, except as it happened in high school.
I know I had what was called "personality," that I
led a gang of little boys in the neighborhood, that
I was afraid of competition, of games, and of being
left out, and that whenever there was a chance that
I might not be chosen for a game, I would hide
behind a green wooden playhouse and no one
knew I was there. When we had to pair off to
walk in line—for grade school children are always
made to walk in pairs, it seems, for a semblance
of order—I hid. I was afraid to ask anyone to be
my partner, and I was sure no one would ask me.
I had a few fights with bigger girls, when forced;
I was always terrified and always fought so fiercely
that I won a measure of respect that lasted for at
least the rest of that year. Once, in camp, a girl
who always hit me finally drew me out of the
secret world I preferred, and although she was two
years older, I knocked her down and dragged her

for fifty feet along the dirt by her hair. Afterward, for the rest of that horrible summer, she followed me about abjectly, saying, "What can I do for you, Master?" I could not understand this, was seldom more than partially aware of her company, and was only glad she no longer hit me.

One of my very few memories of the nine years I spent at various camps was the year I was in a bunk with girls of all ages up to seventeen; I was eleven. It was rather like a women's house of detention. One girl, named Mimi (I thought this was glamorous), who lived in White Plains (where was White Plains? Undoubtedly more glamorous), who came on the train wearing a starched white organdy dress and had more striped T-shirts than I had ever seen outside a store, was the ringleader. One night she encouraged the other girls to tie me up and lock me in a closet with a pillowcase over my head. Later, one afternoon, I was alone with this Mimi. I told her that none of the other girls really liked her, that her best friend (the only one who had not participated in my midnight hazing) liked her least of all. To my surprise she started to cry. She cried until the hollow where her knee was folded under her was filled with tears, like a little pool. I looked at this pool of tears, wondered what sorrow and disappointment were, what made people cry, and why I had been able to attain this power over her. Most of all I marveled at the sight of so much water. She never bothered me again.

Reality was ugly and strange; also it had a simplicity that was like a riddle. At the right words dragons became mice, hurt was inflicted no more, the coward was queen. I did not understand this, nor try to. My private world made sense. It was to my private world with its own people that I retreated. Perhaps it was this that made me a victim, although I suspect children are always looking for a victim and the youngest makes the most logical one. I was always the youngest. I graduated from eighth grade at eleven. But my mother told me that the girls at camp (the year of the closet and pillowcase) did not like me because I read a comic book on the train going up to camp instead of making friends with them. Perhaps she was right; certainly I never doubted her until now.

But about my world. . . . The doctors say this dream world of the strange child is more real than reality, that all the senses are involved in it instead of real life. In other words, food is eaten but not really tasted, the child speaks, responds, and acts

as much as possible like a normal child—sometimes
even more because he tries so hard to deceive—but
without any idea of what human feelings are like.
He seldom loses his temper. His gratification urges,
which in a small child are many and primitive, are
all in the fantasy world; thus, toilet training is simple ("You learned right away," my mother said),
thumb sucking ("You never sucked your thumb")
and touching himself in forbidden places (never
mentioned, never happened) are no problems for
the parents. All sex, sensation, pleasure, in fact all
of life itself, occurs in the fantasy world. In the
real world the child watches as an outsider, tries
his best to imitate what is expected of him, and
often deceives the parents so successfully they
never know he really isn't there.

My dream world, which I remember clearly, consisted of two things. One was my five girls. I think
there were five. The Quints were receiving much
publicity at the time, and the real world sometimes
comes in to reinforce the fantasy one. But my five
were different. They were all the same age, but
each was different: one dark, one blonde, one
medium, and so on. They were dressed identi-
cally, by me, at the start of each day, each in the
same dress and hat but in a different color. Each

had a name. One was named, I now think, for my mother. But not realistically for my mother; named by a diminutive for her name, which I invented. Of course, I had no idea it was my mother, for I worshiped her, and the nickname I gave my imaginary girl was one no one in the family used. This girl was blonde (my mother is dark) and the leader of the others. She was the bad one, the independent one, and of course the one I had to torture (or punish) the most. Perhaps there were not five, but only four. I really cannot remember. My mother was one of four sisters; I had three doting aunts. I wish I could remember the names of my other imaginary subjects, for they might give a clue as to who they really were.

Each morning I awoke, vomited (this never bothered anyone in the family very much after a while, for they were used to it; they left a paper bag beside my bed), and began my fantasy. I told my girls what to wear. One always wore blue, one always green, one always yellow, and my leader (who I now think was my mother) wore red, to show that she was the most important one. She had a red dress and a red beret on her bright blonde hair. My girls were with me all through the day. I told them what to do, they protested of course, and then I had to beat them. Since beating them gave me great sexual pleasure, I usually saved that for nighttime when I was alone in my dark room. Of course they were all afraid of me, adored me, and begged me constantly to love and forgive them. I forgave them after I beat them—but only for a while.

The other part of my fantasy consisted of ghosts. I knew there were ghosts, that they hovered above my window at night and waited to kill me if ever I should show them that I doubted they existed. So every night when I was in bed, I said softly, "I do believe in you, dear ghosts, I do." They hovered above the window in the white curtains, waiting for me to show a sign of heresy, but every night I fooled them. "I don't believe in ghosts," I would tell myself, hiding under the covers, and then, peeking out quickly, I would whisper, "I didn't mean it. I do believe in you, dear ghosts."

Were the ghosts grownups? I wonder. A child has to say, in essence, "I do believe in you, dear grownups." Grownups hate not being respected; they seek vengeance for being tricked. But I knew, on the reality level, that the grownups did not believe in ghosts. My parents told me belief in ghosts was silly. I knew better. I saw the ghosts; the adults did not.

I cured myself of the ghosts when I was about ten. I said, "I don't believe in ghosts," waited, waited for the ghosts to kill me. My heart nearly stopped from panic. But the ghosts did not kill me. "I don't believe in you," I said, perhaps aloud, perhaps in my mind—for aloud and in my mind were the same in those days. Nothing happened. The ghosts hovered, I waited in cold terror, and the ghosts turned into window curtains. I repeated this heresy for several nights and finally discovered that I had won.

My victory over my imaginary satellites was more complicated. Now I know that it had a perfect psychological basis in fact, that the cure I forced on myself came from much the same reasoning enlightened psychotherapists are now using to deal with schizophrenic children in hospitals . . . but of course I did not know any of that at the time, only that it was time to live a different life.

I have to go back for a moment to explain that during those years, starting as far back as I can remember and ending just before puberty, I seemed to be a normally extroverted child. Like many children, I was good at home and naughty in school. You have to be naughty somewhere. But I always did it with such style that no one could really be angry for long. The strange child is abnormally clever. Also, I had the advantage of going to a progressive school where individuality was encouraged and a high IQ went a long way. When I was bad, I was bad with style. When I was in the sixth grade and made to stay after school to do extra homework, and instead left on my desk a caricature of the teacher, Mrs. Piske—her face and the body of a pig—with the caption "Pig Piske," the face was so recognizable that even the stern educator had to laugh. She has kept it to this day. How could a nine-year-old make a recognizable caricature? A child with a secret life can rise to the heights of genius to protect himself in his rare moments of realistic rebellion.

When I was ten and made "cream cheese and jelly sandwiches" out of saltines, library paste, and red ink, they were so real looking that one girl ate three, washed down with milk, until someone told her what I had done. Having fought vehemently for her right to devour as many as she wanted, the girl then ran to the phone to call her mother. Her mother called the principal. "That brat gave my

Barbara paste and ink sandwiches, and her braces are sticking together!" The principal called me to her office. No one was ever called to the principal's office, except for the most cardinal sins. I was not afraid; I was simply calm, numb, aloof. This was no longer happening . . . my prank in the classroom had been a freak, one of those things I sometimes did to prove I was alive, and now it did not exist. But the other kids were very afraid.

The principal looked at me. She had gray hair and rimless glasses. God bless her, for she is dead now, and she was a good and exceptional woman. "If Barbara had eaten only one, I could punish you," she said. "But three. . . !" Greed, I learned that day, was even worse than a practical joke. When I returned upstairs, the entire seventh grade cheered. Eurydice returning from Hades. Two of the boys kissed me, my first kisses. I hardly noticed.

So I was sometimes naughty, but never in real trouble. I did not, for example, do sloppy homework, or fail tests, or talk back. I did what I was told. I kissed grownups if I sensed they would like it. So I was considered affectionate. I played with the little girls my mother told me were the nice little girls to play with. My tantrums were private, behind the shut door of my bedroom, so I emerged cheerful and extroverted again. The grownups said, "Don't let her lose that love of life." What love of life? I did not know what life was. I had my five little girls, in their different color dresses, to be tormented and forgiven, and that was my life. I never dreamed of going to a party, a dance, or on a date. No one wanted me to, for I was a child, so all was well.

At camp I braided lanyards in Arts and Crafts, drew pictures for the mimeographed camp newspaper, played Lady Macbeth to howls of laughter from the audience. The dramatics counselor—the only person or thing that ever had a smell to me, and whom I loved because she smelled of cold cream, which was a sophisticated and exotic smell —told my mother I should study acting in New York because I had talent; my mother said no. I did not protest. To me, there was no future, no growing up, no New York, although I wanted desperately to act. On Saturdays, during the winter, I listened to the Lux Radio Theater, *Stars over Hollywood*, or whatever it was called then, and waited breathlessly to hear a second or two of what it was like to shoot a Hollywood film. I never found out. The program offered a phonograph record—

for one dollar—of an actual movie set, with all the sounds thereof, and to tantalize the prospective customers they began, "Lights, action, camera . . ." and then fadeout. Every Saturday I listened, ear pressed to the radio, hoping some Saturday they would tell one thing more, that perhaps I could hear some more of the mystery if I listened hard enough. It never occurred to me to ask my parents for a dollar, which I am sure they would have given me. Mysteries were logical to me. The forbidden was logical. Life was forbidden, a mystery. How could you ask your parents for a dollar to solve the mystery of life?

But it was the very mystery of life that saved me from what could have been a terrible thing. The doctors say today that if these special children cannot escape their dream worlds by twenty, they usually have a complete breakdown and sometimes can never touch both feet onto reality again. Since it is so difficult to discover who these special children are, many of them are left to the luck of a natural cure. The natural cure occurs in different ways, sometimes simply through the process of change of environment and growing up.

I have to explain that I spent my childhood in Brooklyn, and that Brooklyn is not at all what people think from reading popular novels. To be sure, there are slums, but there is also a part of Brooklyn, Eastern Parkway, which used to be like Park Avenue; a part called the Grand Army Plaza, complete with statuary, which looks like either Washington Square or the Arc de Triomphe; and another part, President Street (where my grandfather lived), which is like any suburb in a small town in the United States. I climbed trees, played handball against the sides of buildings, walked knee-deep through fallen leaves, threw snowballs, and watched magnolias grow. I found worms after rain, played with stray cats, planted a lump of sugar under a pine tree under the assumption that it would grow into a sugar tree, and did all the things other children do in our glorified Midwest. This in Brooklyn. Nobody mugged anybody, and we went a lot to the children's library to hear a sugary-voiced lady read Peter Rabbit aloud.

My best friend was named Sandra. She had red hair, which fell to her waist in waves, assuring her of an enduring role as the Princess, Good Fairy, or heroine of whatever play the class was doing that year. People would stop us in the street to say, "My, what red hair!" I worshiped her, not because I thought she was beautiful, but because she could talk fresh to her mother and grandmothers on both sides and get away with it. Her father lived in Florida and wore a turquoise ring and blue jeans, and, it was rumored, went out with ladies. Altogether, a glamorous figure to all of us. Sandra and I were so devoted that when it was time for either of us to go home from the other's house, we would hide, usually in the shower or under the bed, so we could stay longer. But best of all, Sandra and I had a secret game.

The game was called Ritz Top Torture Academy. No one, not even the other kids, knew about it. We never agreed not to tell, we simply knew. Psychiatrists might call it play therapy. We loved it. On quiet Sundays, while our mothers were drinking tea under the Tiffany glass lamp in the big house on President Street, Sandra and I would be out in the back yard playing Ritz Top Torture Academy.

Once in a while my mother or her mother would look out the back window and say, "Why are you girls making so much noise?" But no one ever investigated, and no one ever knew. The essence of the game was simple. One of us was Miss Ritz Top, and the other Miss Plushbottom. The roles were alternated on different Sundays, but they were essentially the same. Miss Ritz Top and Miss Plushbottom were the directors of a chic girls' boarding school. The pupils, who were children (we were grownups), were in actuality the grownups we knew—her mother, my mother, our teachers, the mother of our other best friend, Alice, who did not allow her to eat candy, and made her drink buttermilk, eat prunes, and go to bed at nine o'clock; Alice therefore needed to be avenged.

When the imaginary mothers of our imaginary pupils came to see our imaginary boarding school, Miss Ritz Top and Miss Plushbottom were as sweet as could be. See our lovely school? Isn't it nice for the girls? But then, when the mothers departed, leaving us with our charges, the torture began. And it was unlimited. We tied the pupils (our mothers, teachers, etc.) to railroad tracks when trains approached, strapped them in front of whirring buzz saws, whipped them, starved them. The *Perils of Pauline,* which we were too young to have seen, were mild in comparison to what Miss Ritz Top and Miss Plushbottom had in store. A major part of this torture was the cries for pity from the victims, acted out by Sandra and me, and the noises of the whipping, buzz saw, train, etc., also acted out by us. We threw stones at the back

of the house; once we even broke an entire barrel-
ful of dishes that someone had left out to be collected by her favorite charity. We yelled, we
roared, we pleaded, we cried for mercy, we laughed
like fiends, we flailed our arms about, we acted
out every hostility known to Freud, Havelock Ellis
and little children, and we had a marvelous time.
Whenever our mothers told us to tone-down-the-
noise-a-little, we looked innocent. When we were
left alone again, we played the best part of the
game: Visitors' Day. That was the day when
the parents of our poor charges came to inspect
the school. Then the girls were unstrapped from the
railroad tracks or the buzz saw and were made to
tell their parents very earnestly that school was
just wonderful, Miss Ritz Top and Miss Plushbottom were as kind as could be, yes the food was
ample, there were games, and they were learning
a lot.

Which of us has not been forced to lie about
school? The grownups ask, How is school? Silly
question. Say you like school, your parents ad-
monish, or people will think you are dumb. School
is fine, the children say. Yeah, it's okay. So the
children-grownups at the Ritz Top Torture Academy told their parents they loved our school, the

parents went away deluded, and Sandra and I began our tortures with renewed vengeance.

Each of us imagined whom we looked like. We looked, of course, like our principals. Now, our principals were kind women, and actually I liked them, especially the prettier one—the one I chose to look like—and our choice of appearance was in no way due to hostility toward these two women. Actually, it was to give Sandra and me real authority. We looked like the principals. So we were Authority, we could do no wrong, we were accountable to no one. We never tortured our principals; we simply chose to look like them.

I think it was this game, my play and companionship with my friend, and something else, that helped me save myself from my dream world. The something else was high school. It had been decided that I would go to private school in New York, which involved long subway trips to be interviewed by strange people in new places. I was only eleven when I was being interviewed, but in order to prove that I would be mature enough to go to high school, I was allowed to wear high heels— those short, thick heels known in the '40's as Cuban heels—silk stockings, and lipstick. I also had a whole suit, not a skirt and blouse, but a real grownup's suit that matched. With it I wore an actual hat, not a child's hat, but a teen-ager's hat, made of matching tweed, with a feather. I had never felt so grown up. "You're only eleven?" the admissions officer or whoever she was would say. And then came grown-up respect. "When we heard you were only eleven, we weren't even going to let you come to be interviewed; but now that we've seen you . . ."

I realized, gradually, that there was going to be a new, different life. Other people, another city, everything new. A place where I wasn't eleven, but a high school student. A school with uniforms, cafeteria food, dances in the gym. Movies! Theater! New York! Maybe even boys! Suddenly I knew there was something out there in the world that other people experienced, although I had no way then of knowing that what it was was life. All I knew was that it was different, that in order to be part of it I would have to know real people, and that my five slaves would have to go away or I would never be able to do these mysterious, exciting things with the other people.

At home in my bedroom on Eastern Parkway I devised a way to get rid of my five (or four?) children. I didn't want to lose them and they didn't want to go, but I knew they must. I shut them in a large chest and sat on the lid. Not literally, of course, but who is to know what was literal and what was not? I imagined a huge packing crate and thrust the five of them into it, with my favorite victim, the blonde leader in her red beret, last and most protesting of all; and I held that lid down. For several days and nights I heard their piteous cries. "Let us out! Please, please let us out!" Sometimes they pushed so hard against the lid that it started to rise open no matter how hard I held it down, but I only pushed harder, *willed* it closed, and finally, after a week, their cries were still. They had gone.

It was strange to be free of them. I felt as if I had grown up. I had dominated them, but I knew instinctively also that they had somehow dominated me. They had occupied my every waking moment. Now I was free of them. They were really gone. They did not return at night to deserve beatings; they did not appear in the morning to ask me what dress to wear. Now there were real girls to meet, to like or hate, to be friends with, play with, or fight with.

Sandra went on to high school in Brooklyn, and except for once or twice, we never saw each other again. We never again played Ritz Top Torture Academy, and for some unspoken reason we never mentioned it to one another, not even as a reminiscence. It was a part of our childhood, a secret part, and it was over. I think if we ever thought about it at all, we remembered it as amusing.

I have not thought of these days of my childhood for many years. I supposed that every child had a secret world, that it was natural, and that the secret world would of course be more real than the world children lived in. Now I know that was not true. Perhaps what seemed so natural to me is, in fact, a case history. I wonder. What I like to think, being like many people a hypochondriac and an egotist, is that for several years I was crazy, and that because of some beautiful thing that called to me—perhaps life, perhaps sanity itself—I cured myself, and it was all so natural, this cure, that I never even thought about it until that evening last summer in the country when a friend began to talk of the advances in therapy with schizophrenic children, and I suddenly remembered a strange world that had served me until the time I understood that I could no longer afford to serve it.

2

Goon

Being reborn is numbness, pain, and pleasure, in that order. If you have been dead and are slowly coming to life, the awakening is a painful feeling first, because it is pain you became dead to avoid. When you are alive again, and the first pains have been lived through, then slowly the happiness begins. Simple things: The sky is clear and blue. A tree. One tree, not a blur of many. A tree that does not bring back a memory of lying under a tree wishing to be dead, but a tree without memory or complication, simply a tree that was never seen before. Shape and color. Black and brown branches . . . leaves. Leaves of many shades of green, not one. And then the smell of the air. The texture of the tree, for soon you want to touch it—tentatively at first because you are still afraid. The combination of tactile texture, scent, and color is a dizzying one. You hold back, wondering if there will be memories after all, old feelings instead of new ones . . . and then you remember that even the old feelings cannot kill any more. And now you have power.

Not you. I. I was dead; I am alive. I said "you" just now because for a moment I was still afraid. When I was a child, I used to think of myself as "she," never "I." "She is walking down the street," I would tell myself, or "She is getting dressed for school," and then I knew it was happening. "This is what she is wearing the day she has an adventure." An adventure meant the day "she" dressed with special care, from the choice of underwear to the coat and what was in the coat's pockets, for the adventure meant the day "she" would finally disappear and be free. She would be walking down the street on her way to school, and suddenly there would be no more home or family or daily events, but simply the adventure. She would never go back, but on to something wonderful. What that wonderful thing was to be I didn't know. There would be people: strangers, but not frightening. Her clothes had to be chosen with special care the day of the adventure, for she would never have any others. They would have to be her favorite clothes, and since I didn't have any particularly favorite clothes, I invented some. Something practical but nice, and a durable coat. I never thought about taking money. The few things I would need I would find or be given. Now when I read in the newspapers about a child who disappears, with the description the frantic family gives the police of what the child had on, I always think how very odd the combination of clothes and colors is, chosen as if they were the last clothes the child would ever take from that house. Was this child going away to find the adventure?

I don't mean a child who has been kidnapped, or one who is too young to know the difference. I mean the little girls who start walking, and then manage transportation, and are finally found safe, hungry, and slightly amnesiac. Sometimes I even wonder about the ones who go off with the Nice Stranger who turns out to be Death in the guise of a wino janitor. Did she think, before Death turned out to be another incomprehensible grownup, that he was at last the adventure?

As I began to come alive, I began to think of death. Before that it had not been necessary. I thought I was the only person in the world who had considered suicide so young, until one girl in my class at high school confessed to her friends that she had often considered it, and they then confessed they had, too. I was shocked at their death wish; I thought it selfish, neurotic, and unrealistic. I didn't tell them of mine, because I thought mine made sense. I had decided, one summer afternoon when I was fourteen, to kill myself because a book of poems I had submitted to a publisher had been rejected. It did not matter so much that he had rejected them, but that I had already told two of the girls at school they would be published. I couldn't face them because I would be worthless again. In fact, that I considered myself so worthless was the reason I decided not to remove myself from the world that particular day. To do so would have involved swallowing my mother's entire bottle of pain-killing capsules, and I knew she would consider my last act on earth typical of my selfishness.

All through high school and college it was the one dream of my life that I would be walking down the street with a friend, and as we passed a newsstand, I would say, "Stop!" Then I would fling open a copy of a current magazine, preferably *The New Yorker,* and point to my first published story. And in that one moment my friend would start to love me. I did not have any particular friend in mind when I had this daydream . . . sometimes it was someone I hardly knew or even someone I had invented. Who it was did not matter; I was not choking from unrequited love but from the close walls of my own grave. In this grave I had heard the word love spoken a million times . . . I-love-you. We-love-you. You-don't-love-us. Do-you-love-me? Love waited to feed on my corpse . . . I will-always-love-you-no-matter-what-because-you-are-my-child . . . while Like hovered a little distance away waiting for the remains . . . They-don't-like-you-any-more-because. Because why? Because you are bad. But will they like me again if I am good? Yes, if you are good.

The party over, the guests gone, the door closes. Tell me what I did wrong. Tonight you didn't do anything wrong. I never know when I did something wrong, so how will I know when I didn't? You'll learn.

I will fight you forever, giver and taker of the words love and like, I will fight you and your words forever. But how will I know you in your varied disguises? I will find a disguise of my own: laughter, mine and that of others.

What idiot poet invented the phrase "the innocent laughter of children"? Watch children at a puppet show, laughing to see the puppet being hit over the head. Their innocent laughter is, more than anything else, nervous laughter. Children need a victim because they are small and vulnerable. Once there is a victim, he is the sacrifice that keeps the others safe.

I think I have discovered now what it is that makes some victims forgive the tormentors of their childhood, even forget them, while most carry the taunts and slights with them all through their lives. Everyone knows people who are constantly exacting penance from ghosts—because once they were too fat, or too thin, or too small, or too tall, or too poor, or made fun of, or ignored. Whenever they are about to step through the doorway into some happy place, they remember again that they were somebody's victims, and turn away. Who cannot remember at least one moment in his life when he was different from everybody else and was made to pay for that difference? Most of us pay for it again later, at the analyst's or in our hearts.

But some people, with no visible help whatsoever, forget even years of ostracism. Some thread of love must have held them together until they had grown up and grown strong. It need only have been a thread of love, but pure and unbreakable, stronger than all the attention and care and false utterances of love children are handed dutifully, like vitamins.

Of all children who were victimized by other children, I remember in particular my friend Goon. Her real name was not Goon, of course, and I even dimly remember a few days or weeks before she became Goon and was just the new girl in class. I think she came to our school (or our class at least) in the fourth grade, because I remember the particular schoolroom where I first noticed her. The desks were small, with slanted, hinged wooden tops, and we were studying the ancient Greeks. The teacher still wrote unfamiliar words on the blackboard. The new girl was different from the rest of us. To start with, her clothes

were different . . . or is that really what it starts
with? Perhaps I should start with her atmosphere.
She was docile, good, and the most intelligent girl
in the class by far. Her IQ, my mother later told
me, was 170. We knew immediately, instinctively,
that she was a good and docile little girl; it made
us all uneasy and angry at her. She was neither a
goody-goody nor a tattletale; she was just good,
and children smell out goodness the way a watch-
dog smells fire. You get one good child in the
group and the whole structure of childhood tyr-
anny begins to be threatened; the other children
have to protect their rights as tyrants, they have
to make the good one suffer.

The second thing that made her different was
her appearance. Secretly, I liked her clothes . . .
they were just the kind of dresses I would have
liked to wear for an adventure. I remember only
two of her dresses—perhaps she had only two—
but I always remember them immaculate and
freshly pressed. Both were of a neat, subdued plaid,
with a row of little silvery buttons down the front
of the bodice. In the center of each silvery button
was a tiny raised thistle. The best thing about these
buttons was that they were not too shiny. She wore
a dark beret, dark knee socks, and brown oxfords.

Between the socks and the hem of her dress pro-
truded her bony, scabbed, and calloused-looking
knees.

She was skinny and too tall for her age, the
kind of girl who will grow up to have a figure
other women will envy, but at eight and nine is
going to have a lot of fights. Her hair was medium
brown, so wild and kinky it seemed silvery at the
edges, like a nimbus of vulnerability. Her eyes
were clear blue, but hidden behind thick glasses
so only our mothers noticed them. Her skin was
like white silk, her teeth small and very white too,
but her face hadn't grown up to her nose yet and
she looked like a shy, sad crane. We all knew at
once we could be mean to her.

No one gives a signal when to be mean to
whom; it simply starts. A boy knocked the dark
beret off her head in the school playground, the
next time someone grabbed it and ran away with
it, soon a group of boys took to waiting outside the
school building in the afternoons to grab her beret
even though her mother was there. The girls did
their share of hit and run, but what they did most
of the time was meaner; they left her out. The
only times they included her in their games were
when being chosen was worse than being left out.

When they played "Farmer in the Dell," she was always the Cheese, and when they crowded around her clapping their hands, they tried to catch the tip of her nose between their palms.

I was her only friend; she loved me; so I named her Goon. Immediately and forever the whole class called her Goon. For years I remember her mother saying to me, "Stop calling Alice 'Goon'; *call her Alice!*"

I would turn to Alice and say, "You like being Goon, don't you?" and she would shrug. "You see?" I would say to her mother, my mother, our teachers. "She *likes* being Goon."

I don't know whether she really minded Goon or not, but one day she decided to dignify her nickname by making it into a whole name. It was the winter Sandra had been taken out of school to be with her father in a warm climate. I was alone without Sandra and our game of Ritz Top Torture Academy, so I tried to find some game that would be a little like it to play with Goon. I knew I couldn't share Ritz Top Torture Academy with Goon; she didn't have the right kind of imagination. We tried several games, based loosely on what we were reading of medieval castles and haunted houses, but none of them were satisfying. One afternoon, while our mothers were trailing behind, Goon and I had a violent snow fight. We didn't even bother to make proper snowballs; we just grabbed hunks of snow and flung them at each other. Goon was a foot taller than I was, although I think we weighed the same, which is not altogether to her discredit since my mother was a disciple of the three-spoons-of-cod-liver-oil school.

I was getting wet and cold from the snow, and the fight did not interest me much, so I ended it by flinging a handful of mushy snow against Goon's glasses, temporarily blinding her like a car without a windshield wiper. She seemed enraged, but she could not find me, and since I had already received several bruises from her bony elbows, I threw myself on top of her, knocked her down into the snow, and made her cry. As soon as she started to cry, we both knew the fight was over, and she got up and stopped crying. Our mothers were still running after us, frantically trying to wipe us off and make peace, when Goon and I were already hand in hand trying to get away from them and tell secrets. We stopped on top of the subway grating so we could feel the whoosh of air from the trains.

"I am Gooney Ghosthead," Goon announced to
me.

"Why?"

"Because I want to be. You can have a whole
name too if you want, but I want to be Gooney
Ghosthead. Goon is short for Gooney Ghosthead."

I thought about that for a minute. I think it was
the only time in my childhood, until years later
when I began to have all sorts of feelings, that I
had a feeling. It was more than an instinct; it was
a human feeling mixed with understanding. I realized she was asking me for a favor. I felt the mild
pain of perhaps the only moment of love I had felt
in years. I hated "Gooney Ghosthead," it was a
stupid name, only a goody-goody grind intellectual
like her could have thought it up, I thought resent-
fully . . . and yet, I didn't want to hurt her any
more.

"All right," I said, "you're Gooney Ghosthead.
It'll be our secret name; we won't tell the other
kids."

She rather liked the idea of a secret; besides, she
was a more than perceptive child and she sensed
what it would cost me with the class to give her
even that much. From then on we both knew that

whenever I called her Goon it was not because she was an oddity but because it was short for Gooney Ghosthead, a nickname given with love.

She even took my side against her mother, the only time Goon ever disagreed with her mother at all. When her mother would start the Don't-call-her-Goon business, Alice would say, "It's not Goon, it's Gooney Ghosthead, and I like it."

She was on my side, but I was on her side only when we were alone. When we were in class, I joined with the others against her, not because I liked it particularly, but because they didn't trust me either and I knew if I kept them concerned with her, they would give me some peace. Goon always seemed to understand. The boys could make her cry when they hit her, and the girls whispering in corners could make her look even more like a shy, sad crane than ever, but when I grabbed at her flailing skinny legs as she pulled herself across the parallel bars in the playground, she only smiled at me through her panic and pretended she thought it was a game.

Sixth grade was a hard year for both of us. First of all, Sandra was away, and Sandra had been my bodyguard. She was big, tough, and popular. Nobody dared touch me when Sandra was around.

Secondly, Goon and I were nine years old, and the rest of the class was eleven. Eleven is the year that begins to separate the women from the girls, the threshold of puberty, the year the grownups get around to telling you about reproduction even though you know most of the dirty words for the act that causes it, and the year the girls who begin to menstruate stand around in little groups whispering, half proud, half horrified.

One day when the little group was knotted together in the classroom, I had the gall to approach them. They giggled, looked at one another, and decided to have some fun.

"Are you Mandrake the Magician?" they asked me, and shrieked with laughter.

Mandrake the Magician . . . he was a man . . . who were they trying to kid? "Sure," I said.

That made them laugh even more. They knew I was only nine years old; I couldn't possibly be Mandrake the Magician. As for me, I had been blessed with such an instructive and boring sexual education from my parents that I didn't even know they were making up another word that began with *m*.

"Prove you're Mandrake the Magician," they said.

If they wanted me to be some dumb comic strip character, I would say I was. But then I spoiled it. "I am," I said, "and you're Lothar."

That sent them off into shrieks. They knew then and forevermore that not only was I not Mandrake the Magician, but that I didn't even know what it was.

The funny thing was, I knew about things that made Mandrake the Magician a bore. But they never imagined I did, so I was left with Goon. After school, sometimes, Goon came to my house. Her strange behavior there gave me stories to use to insinuate myself back into the group again. Her mother never let her eat candy, I could report, and she made Goon drink buttermilk. Every one of us knew buttermilk was not only disgusting tasting, but it was also practically medicine. Goon's mother made her eat prunes instead of candy. She said she wanted Goon to have a good complexion when she became an adolescent. And she didn't want Goon to get fat when she grew up. You obviously had to be really terrified of your mother to let her put over a story like that.

Once in a while, although rarely, I was allowed to go to play at Goon's house. She lived in a small apartment in what I now realize was a very modest neighborhood. She lived with her parents and her grandmother. From bits of conversation I overheard elsewhere, and the tone of voice in which they were said, I realized that adults who were not Goon's parents thought it was a great hardship for a young girl to have to grow up in an apartment with an aged grandmother and only one bathroom. Actually, I thought it would be nice. My grandmothers were both dead, and although Sandra had told me secretly she would let me have one of hers because she had two, she said I had to take the one she would let me have, and so I refused. I figured whatever Sandra was going to give away free had a trick to it somewhere, even if it was a grandmother who didn't know she had been given away and wouldn't even bake me a cookie.

I don't remember much about Goon's grandmother, only impressions I had . . . a lady, very old, dressed in black, who spoke hardly any English, and who loved Goon. I wondered if old ladies spent all day in the bathroom, or if they had to be watched there so they wouldn't fall into the bathtub and die. I never thought about whether or not she baked cookies. It didn't seem to matter. What was most miraculous of all was that Goon seemed to be able to understand some of the foreign language the old lady spoke and to be able to speak to her in it. It was as if the two of them had a secret that only grownups had.

Goon had two other strange and special things at her house, which none of us had: a radio in her room and a microscope. The microscope was of course the more spectacular, but not to me. We did spend a few rainy afternoons looking through the lens at water, dust, and samples of our own blood, but I had seen a microscope at school and it seemed too educational to be fun. But the radio . . . ! To me, a radio of one's own, in one's own room, was so much more than a radio—it was a whole world. It was respect. Every family had a radio, a big one, in a brown wooden cabinet, which stood in the living room or the front hall of the family apartment and was turned on reverently in the evenings. My father listened to the six o'clock news while we were having dinner, my aunt and uncle listened to the symphony on Sundays, and on Sunday night I was allowed to eat my supper in front of the radio while listening to Jack Benny. Everyone knew you had to watch a radio; you sat in front of it and you didn't wander around the room or talk to anyone. Our maid, Angela, had special permission to stop work every afternoon at five o'clock so she could crouch down reverently with her head against the radio and hear what was happening to Young Widder Brown.

But nobody, nobody who was still a child, had a radio in her own room . . . or at least no one I knew of. My older cousin had made a radio and a radio transmitter which could broadcast for a whole block, and I read his satiric commercials into a microphone while he was still pounding them out at his typewriter and handing them to me like an ace reporter. The neighbors across the courtyard would watch us, leaning on their window sills, and hear my voice coming out of their radio. Most of the time, though, my cousin played records on his "radio station," since radios were supposed to entertain the whole family and we both ran out of jokes quite fast. But everyone knew my cousin was good with electrical things, and besides, he was seven years older than I. Goon was my age and she had a radio in her room.

Goon's radio was made of what looked like red plastic (that was another funny thing, something so bright belonging to her), and she was allowed to pick her own programs. I supposed she listened to dull educational things, since she wouldn't have enough guts to turn on *I Love a Mystery* when the lights were out. I was allowed to have a radio in my room when I was sick in bed, and on those occasions I listened to one soap opera after another until I had a headache and was covered with perspiration. I didn't much care about the stories of the soap operas; it was just the idea of listening to them that I liked. I knew that married women listened to them all day, too, and followed the stories all year. Just like in the stories on the radio, I knew that these women spent all day in their kitchens, making coffee and greeting neighbors who dropped in to tell them their troubles or advise them about the men they knew. But after all, that life was only when I was bedridden. Goon could go into her bedroom when she was perfectly well and shut the door and tune in the secrets of the universe.

Goon's father was a druggist—I think he owned his own small neighborhood drugstore—and I remember he used to bring her little things from the store: a bit of soap, a comb, some cologne. Everybody else's father went-to-business, except mine, who was the principal of a school, and the father of the girl down the block from me, Boobra Delerious Mole-in-a-Hole, who was a doctor. Boobra Delerious Mole-in-a-Hole lived in an apartment house with a doorman—a tall, fat, nasty doorman in a uniform, who chased the kids out of the lobby —which meant that she was rich. But her father couldn't bring her pills from work, nor could anyone else's father bring home things from work, and although my father had brought me a frog and a toad in a cardboard house he had made and a jar full of newts in water, there wasn't much else from school he could bring that was exotic. It was exciting to have a father who was a school principal, because whenever I told other kids what he did for a living, they would stare at me with respectful round eyes and breathe, "Ooh, aren't you scared of him?" They never could understand that if he was my father, he wasn't *my* school principal, and I was shrewd enough not to enlighten them.

I had figured out from other bits of conversation I had overheard among the ladies that it was a hard life to be a druggist and there was supposed to be something embarrassing and sad about it. A druggist had to work at night, he could be held up by gunmen, and he didn't make money. It was an odd feeling to know that something was embarrassing and sad, and yet to know that it was somehow wonderful. I didn't know what to believe. A drugstore was looming urns of colored water, brown jars of strange powders and poisons with crumbling labels written in Latin, and a dark, lonely back room where these powders were measured out into little capsules. But a drugstore was also bright lights in a front room, and bottles of perfume with gold threads around their necks, lipsticks, dusting powders with white fluffy puffs, blue and pink soaps wrapped tightly in cellophane. I pictured a never-empty storehouse of glittering cosmetics, a place from which, when she grew up, Goon could always bring home things to make her become beautiful. I think she must have felt the same way, because she used to show me the little souvenirs her father brought her, and at those moments she seemed almost self-possessed.

Goon was an only child, as was I, and indeed as were most of my friends. No one we knew had more than one sister or brother. We were all born at the height of the Depression; also, the Margaret Sanger Clinic had come out with a wonderful new device. My mother told me that no one she knew used this device because it gave people cancer . . . nevertheless, we were all only children, each of us had her own room, and we went to private school. When pressured, my mother told me that God just hadn't sent her any more children, but most of the time she liked to say that I was so perfect she knew she could never have another one like me, so she had stopped. Whenever she told me I was perfect, I wondered what was so terrible about me that she would have to lie this way to cover up. Since my cousin was an only child, too, my private answer to the question of why there were no more children was that God had put a blight on all the women in our family.

Being only children was annoying to all of us because the catch-phrase of the day was that Only Children were Spoiled. Whenever we did anything wrong, we were reminded how spoiled we were, and strangers had a rude way of asking, when they found out we were only children, "Aren't you spoiled?" I assumed I was, and I wondered if Spoiled was the evil thing about me my mother was always trying to hide. Goon, my mother often told me, had not been spoiled. "Alice's mother is strict, and Alice-loves-her-for-it." Proof that Goon loved her mother was that Goon was obedient, respectful.

There were two schools of thought in child psychology at that time: be permissive, and be strict. Most of the mothers flapped around like chickens, trying to decide whether to be permissive or strict, and always worrying that some other mother was doing the right thing. Goon and I both had the throwing-up problem—we would wake up in the middle of the night and inconvenience everybody but ourselves by vomiting in bed. The difference between us was that Goon had been cured of this orneriness right away, while I kept at it, on and off, for years. My mother told me that Goon's mother had cured her by making her sleep in the vomit. "I ought to make *you* sleep in it."

Just try it, I thought, and I'll take a big hammer and smash your head in. As for Goon's mother, she was one of the charter victims of the Ritz Top Torture Academy when Sandra was around to play it with me. I never told Goon I knew about the sleeping-in-it, or about the fantasy punishment I visited on her mother . . . I thought it might upset her.

Goon's mother was an extremely brilliant woman, an Intellectual, who used careful diction and wore somber, practical clothes and rimless spectacles. She presented herself at school every day at three o'clock to take Goon home. Instead of protecting Goon from the assaults of the other children, the presence of her mother served to incite them, for it showed undeniably that she was strict (everyone else but Goon and I went home alone like a person). If she had been a pink, fluttery mother, like Sandra's, her presence would not have been such an event, but Goon's mother looked like a teacher. It did not matter to us that Goon lived far away from school; she could have lived in Flatbush for all we cared. "Your mother comes to get you, yah yah!"

Worst of all, Goon seemed glad to see her. I suspected they actually had adult conversations with each other. None of us had conversations with our mothers if we could avoid it; we told them what we were doing in school and answered their questions, we kissed them of course, we collected our allowances from them if our fathers were busy, we let them drag us around the department stores and to the bakery and dry goods store, but we didn't walk down the street talking with them.

I think we all lived in a mother-oriented society in our neighborhood. We never taunted one another about fathers; if someone's father was dead or had run away, we were actually nicer to her. But our mothers' clothes and mannerisms were an integral part of the pecking order.

I remember a fight I had with Boobra Delerious
Mole-in-a-Hole. "Your mother wears a mink coat;
she's no good," she told me.

"Your mother wears a black seal coat," I replied,
"and she looks like a big black sow in it."

"Your mother is a fat pig. And a mink coat is
worse than a seal coat. It costs more."

"A seal coat costs just as much."

"It does not."

"My mother," I announced, "wears a mink coat
to keep warm."

"How do you know?"

"She told me."

"She's a liar."

"I'm going to throw you in that hole."

"Just try it!"

"Your mother . . ." I said, saving the real am-
munition for last, "Your mother feels the tablecloth
at birthday parties, to see if it's linen or only paper."

"How do you know?"

"My mother saw her."

I don't think Goon was invited to many birthday parties. I remember her at only a few. The
chic thing to do in those days was to slip the su-
perintendent of a building a tip and get an empty
apartment for the afternoon so the children would

not mess up one's furniture. The empty apartment, which had not been swept for months, would be furnished with a table, crepe paper decorations, balloons, and party food; then we would spend the afternoon breaking the balloons and throwing the crepe paper decorations and what was left of the food out the windows onto people's heads. Meanwhile, the mother of the Birthday Child would entertain certain other, chosen mothers downstairs in her own apartment with her best tea service. My mother and Goon's mother deplored this practice and took us home from "that dirty apartment" as soon as possible. I think Goon was relieved to get away. Her behavior was slightly hysterical at the parties, always doing something a moment after everyone else, as if she had just then realized it was the thing to do, and although she smiled when she broke balloons, she seemed about to cry. As for me, my mother could always notice more about the party in five minutes than I could in an hour; she would give me an indignant résumé at home. She remembered the water bombs and "the dirt all over your dress," while I only remembered that Goon had looked so desperate trying to be like the rest of us, and how curious it seemed.

Looking back, I wonder whether all the things

about Goon that were different could have been matters of pride instead of flaws if only the grown-ups hadn't tried so hard to cover them up. There was the matter of physical maturity. Goon was bigger, and she had matured earlier than the rest of us, but while we were all pretending things had happened to our bodies that hadn't yet, they had happened to Goon, and she was not allowed to tell. The first day I wore a bra to school, I motioned to Sandra to come over to a secluded corner of the playground.

"Run your finger down the center of my back," I whispered. She did. Her eyes lit up.

"You do it to me," she whispered. I did, and then we giggled and hugged each other.

But a year before, my mother had told me in sepulchral tones that "poor Alice is already wearing a brassière, and you mustn't mention it to anybody." And she was also, horror of wonders, Mandrake the Magician! Poor Goon . . . if we had only known, instead of different, she might have been special.

Yet, with all this—the isolation, the ostracism, the prunes, the buttermilk, the old lady in the bathroom, the embarrassing poverty, the skinny legs and kinky hair—Goon turned out better than

most of the rest of us. I saw her one day at a class
reunion, with her young husband; surprisingly, she
was one of the first of our class to marry. He
looked, to my amusement, exactly like her. They
were sweet and shy with other people, and very
close. He wasn't just a man you bring to a class
reunion to show off; he was the man she wanted.
She seemed proud of her mother, but detached
and a little . . . how can I say it? . . . superior,
as if Goon were at last the grownup of the two.
The kinky hair had been straightened, and Goon
was neither fat, as her mother had feared, nor
pimply. She wore very little make-up, and she was
beautiful. We were in the garden in back of the
school building, a garden none of us had known
existed. When we were children, it had been the
sole property of the principal and teachers. A table
had been put out in the sun, with a white cloth
and a glass bowl full of the innocuous punch
served at school affairs. Goon and her husband
stood side by side, not touching but seeming to be
holding hands. He was shy with the strangers, but
not afraid of anyone. Behind them was a red brick
wall with ivy growing on it. The building seemed
much smaller than I had remembered, the teachers
and mothers older and less important than they

had ever been before. Next to this no longer tall
and skinny, but slim and radiant, Goon, the other
girls looked overdressed and lumpy.

I spoke a few words to her, at a loss for anything
to say. We had become strangers. I had discovered
the prison of my mind, while she had grown out of
hers. I wondered how she had managed to find a
male Goon, exactly like her, but then I thought,
Perhaps it was easy.

I knew the old grandmother had died. Many of
the old people we knew had died; by now we were
accustomed to the deaths you have to take for
granted when you grow up. The one death that
had shocked and saddened me, however, was that
of Goon's father, because although I had hardly
known him, I had recognized a sweetness in him
that had seemed like light. I remember him sitting
in their tiny dark living room, with a sort of trans-
lucence around his kinky hair, the same as Goon's.
She had looked exactly like him.

It is strange how embarrassed people become
when someone dies. They don't know what to say,
even to themselves. I remember the day my grandfather died. He was in his mid-eighties, and very
ill, but still when he died, his children acted as if
it was an inexplicable curse put upon them for

some secret sin. He was still in his oxygen tent in the hospital when I arrived, and the middle-aged children who had suddenly been thrust into the next generation were sitting in the corner weeping bitterly. Endless tears poured down their faces; they were more like children than ever. I remembered a photograph of Pope Pius on his bier, and I thought how much alike all dead people looked —their features turned to bone, the slackened muscles pulling everything away from the bones that are the essence of the face, the skin golden as wax. My grandfather's hand still looked human. I knelt by the bed and held his hand, because when he had been alive and very old, neither of us with anything to say to one another, he had liked to sit in silence with me for a moment, holding my hand.

Suddenly the mourners in the corner stopped crying. My mother's grief turned to a kind of wonder. "How can you touch him?" she asked.

"Why not?"

"But . . . aren't you afraid?"

Yes, we are all afraid of the dead; they remind us of our own death to come. But I was not afraid of him. The small square hand with its tapering fingers and clean white nail-tips, the hand that had hurt me with the strength of its grip, was silent and gentle now in mine. After a while I left the room.

I never saw him again. At the funeral the coffin was closed. The rabbi who officiated at the cemetery seemed to feel he had to drive everyone into a frenzy; he rose to his toes and rocked back on his heels, crying out a prayer, and he incited the mourners to toss flowers into the grave. I heard the flowers hit the coffin . . . splat, splat . . . firm, living stems striking the body of a dead tree. The sound of those flowers beating the coffin offended me—perhaps it sounded louder to my ears than it actually was. While the mourners were straggling back to their cars, I wandered away.

In another part of the cemetery was the small mound of a fresh grave. The land was not yet ready for the weight of a headstone, so until then the grave was marked with a strip of wooden stick and a white tag bearing a name. Last name only: my great-aunt, my grandfather's sister. As I stood looking at the grave that seemed so tiny and alone, I realized that I still had the flower in my hand. I had not had the heart to fling it to reassure the rabbi we were getting our emotional money's worth. I walked over quietly and put the flower on Aunt Rose's grave.

Aunt Rose . . . when I think of you, it is the only time in my life I ever want to cry. I don't cry for sorrow, but for love. I remember you always as old, and tiny, even when I was a child as small as you. I remember where you lived, a musty, strange apartment, where you stood in the kitchen and made me an apple pancake whenever I came to visit. You never asked me questions, you never grabbed me with painful embraces, but your eyes held love. Those were the days when nothing tasted to me, the days of my dream world with its dream people, but I always ate your apple pancake, and you always remembered I liked it and ran to make it for me. I always wished for a little old foreign mother, who would cook something for me and speak in an accent as you did. I wrote to you from camp as I did to no one else. I drew pictures on my letters. Every summer when I went away, you sent me stationery so I could write to you and a box of forbidden lollipops "for a sweet life." I remember the large shiny brown box with the square lollipops, each wrapped in cellophane, each brightly colored. I did not notice colors either, in those days of my dream world, but I noticed the colors of the lollipops you sent me. I liked the chocolate ones best because I had never seen a chocolate lollipop before, so I saved them for last. We were not allowed to have candy at camp, but somehow your candy always got to me, and I hid the box at the bottom of my trunk, under the clothes.

Everyone in the family made a point of loving me, they saved every scrap of letter or poem I ever wrote . . . but you loved me and you saved my letters and you never told. I did not write to you so you would save them, but because you were special. After you died, your children found my letters in your bedroom, some of them twenty years old, breaking at the creases where they had been un-folded and refolded time and again as you reread them. Most of them I did not remember I had even written. They were gay, sweet letters, not like the ones I wrote to anyone else, not even my parents.

When you were too sick and in too much pain to go out of the house, in the last years before your death, too sick even to get the new glasses that would have made you able to read, you still kept my letters. I think the great gift is to be able to love someone and not to have to tell him so. Children always know who loves them and who does not. Love that must always speak of itself is selfish love, feasting on the sound of its own words. When we declare our feelings to the loved one, are we not really asking for an answer in return?

Aunt Rose . . . when I gave you the flower, it was not a flower. I don't know what it was; a word, perhaps. But you knew what it was, just as you always knew the answers to questions everyone else thought they had to ask. I think the reason I cry when I think of you is not so simple as love. I think I cry because I feel free. Freedom, for me, is the painfulness of rebirth. I wish I had lived with you.

I don't know if any of this is very clear to anyone but me. I thought of my great-aunt just now because I was wondering about Goon's grandmother, the old lady whose presence made people feel sorry for Goon. I wonder if her love was the strength Goon had against the other children, against her own mother, against being different and friendless and funny-looking and much too bright.

I just had one last thought, the oddest of all.

If children know who likes them no matter what words are spoken or what silly meanness is visited on them, perhaps I was not so hateful as I remember myself. Goon always found so much pleasure in the scraps of kindness people gave her. Perhaps she even found kindness in me.

3

Baby Love,
Oh Baby Love

So now normalcy—adolescence. High school, New York, world I had dreamed about.

Adolescence is less than a country; it is an island . . . a wild, dark place with moments of blinding white light, where the landscape stretches forever and the markers are few. The people who inhabit it are half savage and full of the beginning of tenderness. They drink blood. They huddle together without understanding why they like whom they think they love, and they break apart without explanation because the smallest thing is reason enough. There is a time in life, just before adoles-

cence begins and when childhood is done, when
you can "love" anyone. I can see how Fagin got
his band of ragged pickpockets, for I am sure they
all loved him. At camp, an all girls camp, we loved
certain counselors madly because one smiled at us,
or because another rode a horse well, or because
another let us see her smoke when smoking was
officially forbidden. I felt flashes of that love, and
I know any counselor with neurotic tendencies
could have enslaved me—and I also know that
after the summer was over I wrote one postcard
and received one, and then never thought about
my love again.

That was when I was twelve. I was too old to be
at ease with boys, and I was too young to like them.
At high school dances in the gym my freshman
and sophomore years no one danced with me, so
I would wait an agonized half hour and then hide
in the locker room fighting tears until the dance
was over and my father came to walk me home
and ask if I had had a nice time. I always told him
yes. Once I told my mother no one had asked me
to dance and I had hidden, and she told me I
should have waited longer. I tried, but I became
too embarrassed, and so I hid again. The girl all
the boys wanted to dance with was older, at least

fourteen or fifteen, and she was beautiful, with straight blond hair that swung all in one piece when she moved. She wore a black dress. I wore a yellow rabbit's-fur-and-wool dress with the top half entirely covered in gold sequins, and my mother had made me a hair band with a spray of gold artificial flowers that extended down to my ear lobe. She put rouge and lipstick on me and told me I looked like "a doll." I'm sure I did, for dolls wear funny costumes and have bright circles of rouge on their cheeks, but they don't look like teen-agers.

The only boy who ever wanted to dance with me was pale as cold cream, with blond hair, acne, and he was thirteen years old. The other girls laughed at him because he wore a pink Brooks Brothers shirt, a style that would be much admired when we were older and were freshmen in college. Like me, he must have been the victim of a mother who tried to make him look pretty instead of fashionable. I was grateful that he had asked me to dance, but I ran away from him into the locker room again because the other girls did not think he was good enough. Four years later he was my date at graduation, and he was the best-looking boy there; but that was later, and when you are twelve years old at a dance, there is no such thing as later. Eleven o'clock, when your torture will be over, is the latest you can imagine. After the dance my father came to pick me up and took both of us to Schrafft's on upper Broadway for a soda. I remember the boy ate a pineapple sundae with vanilla ice cream, and it struck me as the perfect thing for a vanilla-colored blond in a pink shirt, and I was embarrassed and hated him for not eating hot fudge like normal people did. I suppose the pineapple was for the acne, but I was implacable. I had no interest in boys and their problems.

However, I was in love with my first real love. I was twelve, and my first real love was a girl. She was a junior, and I think she was seventeen. She was very tall and thin, with long black hair, and since we were a girls' school, the taller girls had to play the men's roles in our school plays. That year, my first, our school play was *Romeo and Juliet*. She was Romeo. I think half the school fell in love with her that night. She wore a black leotard, I remember, and some brocade thing, and she was very tall and agile and flat chested. She had studied ballet, and her leaps and movements were a thing to behold. Besides all that, she was a good actress. No one particularly noticed the girl who played Juliet, a placid blonde who probably grew up to become a society matron or Miss Rhein-gold.

Our school began with the two-year group and went on through the lower and middle schools through high school, although you could enter at any time. I had entered in the high school, which was bad enough in the pecking order, but worse, I came from Brooklyn, a place all the other girls assumed was inhabited mainly by truck drivers and people who said dese, dem and dose. I remember once a girl said to me in surprise, "You don't talk like you come from Brooklyn," and I said, "What are people who come from Brooklyn supposed to talk like?" She said, "Well . . . you know."

Things let up for me a little in the second year, when a few girls had the audacity to transfer from public schools or lesser private schools in their sophomore year, and then they were the ones who were looked down upon, but the first year was an unpleasant surprise because I realized that no one would ever take me seriously—or my education seriously—because I had been educated elsewhere. My love, the girl who played Romeo, had been in the school since a few minutes after birth, and so she was at the top of the hierarchy, and it was always assumed that some day she would be elected president of the student government.

Our school government, like the Government of the United States, had a unique place in our school society. On the day of the Government Assembly all uniforms had to be neatly buttoned up to the neck (you nearly choked) and down to the wrists; there could be no lumpy objects dragging down the pockets, and everyone stood up straight with glazed eyes, marching quietly down the stairs under the equally glassy eyes of neatly uniformed monitors. We would go into the assembly room, a terrifying marvel of red leather seats with a stage at the front and a balcony at the rear—the same room where the school plays and the Christmas Nativity Festival were put on. Then the President sat on the stage, and we began our meeting. There was a form of democracy and free discussion. The most frightening thing of all was to speak. If anyone had the temerity to speak, it was only after the same kind of deliberation that precedes your first dive off the high tower into a swimming pool. You would hardly hear your own voice for the beating of your heart in your ears, and for at least five minutes after you sat down again you would see black before your eyes while you waited for your heart to

slow down. Most of us spoke only during the nominating and discussion that preceded elections. A
speech for a candidate went something like this:

"I think Suzy would be a good secretary because
she has been at the school for a long, long time,
and because . . . uh . . . she'd be very good. Gulp.
Thank you." And then a plop as the triumphant
speaker fell down in her leather seat. Her friends
seated around her would whisper congratulations
for bravery.

It was no wonder that one was elected to an
office only as the most sincere form of patronage
and admiration, and that planning or even wishing
to be president was something that required an
emotional constitution somewhat akin to the one
required in aiming to be President of the United
States.

But we all knew that Maria—as I shall call her
because that was not her real name—would someday be president, and so she had an aura around
her months before the actual elections began, as
many politicians do when you know they will be
the new light of their party.

Her being the future president was not the
reason I was in love with her. Part of it, I think,
was because she had been Romeo, and even after-

ward, seeing her in the sexless dark blue school uniform that made her look as much like a boy as the Romeo costume did, I thought of her as she had been up on that stage reciting Shakespeare as if it had been real words. Part of it, also, was group hysteria. Everyone was in love with Maria. In fact, that love was how I acquired my best friend.

The first term my best friend was a Czechoslovakian girl from Beverly Hills, California, whose father directed newsreels, and who I was convinced was going to be my entree to becoming a movie star, which was my life's ambition. Because I was in high school, I was now allowed to go about the streets freely, and I had an allowance of a dollar fifty a week, which was to be used for bus fare to the dentist to have my braces adjusted and for other things such as sundaes at the corner drugstore and trips to the movies. Since my best friend was also from out of New York, we discovered New York together. I do not remember much about this six months, except for one late afternoon, just before suppertime, when it had snowed heavily and the sidewalks had all disappeared in a smooth field of white. The sun was down. We stood on the corner together, looking out at the expanse of unsullied snow, new, white, glistening with red and green from the corner traffic light, and we were struck dumb. At last, to me, this was New York as I had always dreamed it was. Of course, by the next morning when I walked to school, the snow was trampled slush, and I do not remember ever seeing another such snowfall in my life. But that may have been because it was my first in New York, and so it was special.

Romeo and Juliet had not yet been presented at school, and so I was not yet in love with Maria. I was a little in love with my best friend, because she came from Beverly Hills (which to me was the same as Hollywood) and because she was nice. She had a personality a little like my old friend Goon—placid and amenable and good—but she was chic and nobody ever thought of picking on her. She told me stories about California, and once her mother took her and her brother and me to the theater to see Helen Hayes. But then at the end of that term the family went back to California, and so I was alone. It was around this time that I discovered Maria, love, and my new best friend, Pam.

Pam I had noticed before, a shy, plump, short girl, very neat, who always had her uniform buttoned up to her chin even when it was not an assembly day, and who never kept lumpy things in her pockets. Her real clothes, which we were allowed to wear under our uniforms, looked like another uniform. She always wore starched white cotton blouses and plain navy skirts. She would watch me with my best friend and look shy, as if she wanted to join us, but we never paid attention to her. I knew she had come up through the middle school and so was one of the elite, but her diffidence made her a victim in my eyes, and I rather enjoyed paying no attention to her because I knew she minded. Then, one day, after my best friend had gone back to California, Pam spoke to me for the first time. "Would you like to be friends with me?"

I thought for a minute. Her openness shocked me. "All right," I said. And so we became inseparable.

I soon discovered that she had a mad crush on Maria. In this one respect Pam was not shy at all. It was at her instigation that we began the weekly routine of sending a flower. We had discovered the apartment building where Maria lived, and spent many long cold afternoons standing in the street looking at her doorway hoping she might appear. She never did, of course, because she was an older girl and had better things to do after school than to go right home. One of these better things was to visit the dramatics teacher, a very dramatic middle-aged widow, who had a select group of favorites who were invited to her apartment to talk about the theater. Pam and I were sure they were all making love, and we detested the teacher; she scared us to death. Full of those desires ourselves, we were nevertheless children, and we were happy with dreams. There was a very fashionable and expensive florist shop a few blocks away, and since Pam and I felt that nothing but the best would do for Maria, we went there and asked how much it would cost to send a single carnation with ferns, fixed as a corsage. The florist looked at us, two twelve-year-olds in school uniforms (Pam was fourteen but looked twelve), and he said it would be twenty-five cents. We could afford that. We were delighted and did not understand why our parents considered it the most expensive florist in New York. Grownups, we knew, were fools, and apt to be rooked. We wrote a sentimental but dignified card to Maria from the two of us and sent her a carnation corsage every week. She never thanked us.

Pam and I spent all our days together when we

were not in classes, and at night we spent hours talking on the telephone, mostly about how we could get Maria to notice us. Once in a while, inventing some elaborate but obviously ridiculous excuse, Pam would call Maria at home and speak to her. Then she would call me, and we would spend at least an hour discussing every nuance of their conversation. I wanted to do it, too, and got up the nerve once or twice, but then one night I did something which must have been the first spontaneous act of my life. I called Maria, armed with my carefully thought-out excuse, and then when she said hello and waited to hear it, I said, "I just called because I wanted to talk to you."

She was very nice about it (after all, a seventeen-year-old girl with homework and boy problems and parts to learn has nothing to say to a twelve-year-old girl who is in love with her), and she spoke to me for a while pleasantly about school as if we were two friends. I could not wait to tell Pam of my triumph.

"I just told her I wanted to talk to her. I couldn't help it; it seemed silly to lie. And it worked! She didn't mind!" Pam's reaction was incredulity and then respect. I called Maria several times after that, at decent intervals of a week or so, always to

talk, and although her responses were less and less
enthusiastic, she managed to keep up a conversation for five minutes, and I felt proud of myself
for acting like a grownup instead of a little kid.

Nevertheless, I knew she was getting bored, if
indeed she had not always been bored with me,
and I knew the only reason she encouraged me at
all was that she rather liked being admired. There
seemed no way in the world to make her like me
as a friend, much less make her return my love,
for I would always be twelve and she would always
be seventeen: I was a freshman with braces and
no knowledge of the world, and she was Romeo,
who got invited to the apartment of the dramatics
teacher.

Once, by some insane bravery, I got Maria to
agree to have lunch with me the next Saturday.
Saturday lunches were the staple of our social life
in high school. Every Saturday you would go to
another girl's house for lunch or invite her to
yours, and then you would go to the movies down
the block, either Loew's or RKO, and see the
double feature. Dates were made weeks and weeks
in advance, and you made dates even with girls
you did not know or like very well because it was
important to fill your Saturdays. This did not apply

to those girls who already knew boys and were dating them on Saturday afternoon or on Saturday night, in which case they spent Saturday afternoon washing their hair. It was only for the little kids. There was such a strict ritual about these Saturday lunch dates that if anyone had or did anything that broke the expected routine, it was viewed with suspicion. I remember one girl, who was more sophisticated and shaved her legs, who invited me to lunch at her apartment. The lunch was served to the two of us by a uniformed maid, which was bad enough, but then she had the temerity to serve something on a crescent-shaped glass side dish which turned out to be lettuce with French dressing. Lettuce! Lettuce was something they put inside a sandwich and which you took out. French dressing! Who ever ate anything but mayonnaise? And if there wasn't a sandwich, what could you eat? I thought there was something peculiar about that girl for years, until I grew up.

At any rate, I had inveigled Maria into a Saturday lunch date. We had agreed to eat at the corner drugstore, which was what the older girls did. But of course, she had to break the date, for she had never intended to keep it. She sent me a very

nice note, on a stiff little white card, in her im-
peccable tiny print:

"Darling, I am so sorry about lunch Saturday.
Please forgive me. Love, Maria."

I must have reread it a thousand times, and I
tacked it up on the cork bulletin board in my bedroom, where it stayed for years, even after I no
longer cared about her at all. I thought that note
was the epitome of charm and sophistication.
Darling!

For years, in fact until after I had graduated
from college, I wrote letters to people the way the
last person had written a letter to me. I had no
idea how to write a letter, except to my Aunt Rose.
I copied others: boys from Princeton, girls from
my past, anyone who seemed to know more about
it than I did. For years I started every letter with
Darling, unless, of course, it was to a boy I liked.

Pam considered my note from Maria a trophy,
since she had never received one, and viewed me
with considerable respect. It was odd, but although
Pam and I were inseparable during the week, we
hardly ever saw each other on weekends or at
home. For one thing, she had a governess. An
actual, real-life, Mary Poppins governess—a stout

German woman who looked stern and bored with us and wasn't like Mary Poppins at all. I had already decided that Pam was the poor little rich girl like Shirley Temple in her teen-age movies, and when I was finally invited to Pam's apartment, I saw why she was so shy.

It was on Park Avenue and was the largest apartment I had ever been in, except for one inhabited by a shrieky school newcomer whose father had made a lot of money in something like handbags and who had an enormous dog that knocked you down. But in Pam's apartment there was no dog, or if there was, it was a tiny, silent dog, and no one shrieked. No parents appeared to say hello. The governess appeared to announce what time I would have to get out and to warn Pam not to get her clothes messed up and to keep me in her room. The governess also said that a little later Pam would be allowed to go into her mother's room to say hello.

Pam's room had twin beds with white spreads and an enormous air conditioner, the first I had ever seen in anyone's home. I knew it must have been frightfully expensive. On top of the air conditioner were many glass jars with avocado pits and carrot tops in water, all of them sprouting leaves. That seemed to be Pam's only hobby. There was no junk—no toys left from childhood, no autographed dog acquired in adulthood, no piles of movie magazines, no photographs of movie stars cut out and pasted on the wall or tacked to a bulletin board as in my bedroom. It was all very grown up and antiseptic—and somehow like a nursery. Pam's starched white blouse and navy skirt seemed right in place in that room. We were both self-conscious and talked little.

Then the governess came in to say that Pam could see her mother now. We both went. Pam's mother's bedroom was such a thing of beauty it took my breath away. It was all done in antiques and subdued lovely colors. Her mother was a writer, and there was a typewriter on the desk. Her mother called out to us from the bathroom and said we could come in, for she was making up to go out that night. Inside the bathroom there was such an array of cosmetics as I had never seen. My mother's entire equipment consisted of a box of powder she must have acquired on her honeymoon and a lipstick of the same vintage, plus one bottle of nail polish which Elizabeth Arden named 1942 when she put it out in 1941 and which still remained on the bathroom shelf although it was now 1943. But Pam's mother had creams and oils and moisturizers and foundations and eye shadows of every color . . . blue! green! gold! She was very beautiful. She was wearing all of them. She did not look at all like a mother, but like a celebrity, which she was.

She was so lovely and secure and cold, she frightened me, and I was almost in love with her; but then she came close to me and I smelled her breath, and I did not like her any more. I was disappointed but not surprised. I had known all along that that was what grownups were like: beautiful and covered up on the outside, but underneath . . . decay.

Then I left, for it was Pam's dinner time, and I never went to Pam's apartment again. I felt I understood her and her need for Maria to love her, for no one seemed to care about her, not even me. My love for Maria, I felt, was different, for I was special and Maria was special, even though she was older and famous in school, and one day Maria had to realize that. I would never give up until she did. We were both special, sensitive; she acted and danced, and I planned to be a writer, in fact I did write poetry, and I drew cartoons for the school paper. We were both gentle and strange. Pam was just lonely and lost. Pam was too different for me to understand, for I could not yet understand anyone who lived like someone in a Shirley Temple teen-age movie. But she was still my best friend, although we were strangers, and we were still inseparable, and neither of us had to ask why she never asked me to go to her apartment again.

Everybody was used to Pam and me being best friends, just as people are used to a couple who has been married for years, and no one asked any questions. The only bond we had was our crush on Maria. One afternoon Pam and I were sitting side by side at the soda fountain at the corner drugstore where all the girls went after school, and we were not saying anything to each other because we had nothing to say. We sat there in total boredom, secure, thinking about the sodas we were drinking. One of the older girls on the next stool was watching us, and then she turned to me and said, "It's wonderful to see two such good friends. You don't even need to talk to communicate."

We were both pleased for a moment to have been noticed by an older girl, to have been complimented, to have been told we had something good and special. Then I was not so pleased. I realized, for the first time, how stupid people were.

The mask people put on was becoming more apparent to me day by day, and I saw how simple it was to live in a way that made everybody satisfied. That was what I had always wanted, to satisfy everybody, and now I was beginning to realize it was not what I needed to be happy. I needed something else. I did not yet know what it was, but I knew fooling people was no longer the answer. Something tough and real in me was beginning to be born.

As we moved closer into the spring of that year, the time for elections came. Emotions came sprouting out in nearly every area of our lives but that one. The election that year was sure to be a shoo-in. Maria would be president by a landslide, although a few other girls would be nominated for appearances' sake—tall, quiet, dignified girls, one of whom as runner-up would probably be elected president of the student council. The third position of power was vice-president, and then there was treasurer and secretary, which were rather boring jobs usually won by girls who were cheerful and enthusiastic and willing to do dull work. I was not quite sure what the vice-president and the president of the student council did, for although they were positions of respect, the one that really counted as a measure of group love was the president.

As I said, emotions were coming out. I remember we had several English girls in our class, girls who had been sent to America for safety because the blitz was going on in London. One of them was a fiery little girl named Kathlyn, who had a permanently mean expression, lank dark hair, and who looked as if she never washed her face and, what was more, never intended to. I was not particularly aware of Kathlyn's existence, because she practiced the cello a lot when the rest of us were wandering around the halls trying to escape study hall, but I was dimly aware that she, too, was one of the girls who was in love with Maria. Then one day Kathlyn burst into my life in a wholly unexpected way. It was about four-thirty, and most of the girls had gone home, except for those who were doing something like painting or sculpting or rehearsing for a play. Classes were officially over at three o'clock, but you were supposed to stay until four-thirty doing something creative, unless you had an excuse to go to the dentist for your braces. Suddenly there was Kathlyn, glowering, and there was I, standing there. She turned on me in fury.

"You stay away from Maria," she screamed. "She's mine!"

That made me smile. Maria belonged to all of us who loved her, but if she belonged to anyone, it was certainly not this grubby little thirteen-year-old. "She's not yours," I said coolly.

"She is mine, I love her, and stop trying to take her away from me!"

Suddenly she had me by the hair and was pulling me down the hall. It hurt more than anything I had ever felt, even the eighty-six splinters I had acquired the time I fell down on the boardwalk. What hurt the most was that she, a near-stranger, was doing this to me because of her wild love for a girl who didn't love her any more than she loved me or any of us. And why me? She dragged me all the way down the hall to a deserted room and then let go, but only to have a free hand to hit me. The room we were in was the nursery, where they took care of several babies of working mothers during the day, and incidentally taught us child care and, supposedly, sex. It still smelled pleasantly of baby oil and security, and Kathlyn was punching me.

"She's mine! Maria is mine!" she kept screaming.

"Who could love you?" I said. She hit me again.

Then the school nurse came in, the one who supervised the taking care of babies and the lessons on sex, and at the sight of her Kathlyn ran away and disappeared. When she had gone, I put my head down on a pile of clean diapers and cried.

"Why are you crying? What did she do?" the nurse kept asking, warm and starchy-white, but I would not answer her. What could I tell her? That we were both crazy? I wanted to be back in the nursery, to be protected, to smell clean babies, and I hated everything about love. I rubbed my scalp to see if she had made me bald, and was re-assured that she had not. After a while I stopped crying and went home. I wondered why I had been too frightened to hit Kathlyn back, and then I decided it was because she was more like a grubby little boy than a girl. But I had hit boys before. And if I was a girl and Maria was a boy, so to speak, then how could Kathlyn be a boy? No, she was a girl. But I had not fought back because the whole thing seemed so ludicrous, fighting a duel over the girl we both loved. Then, slowly, I began to be flattered. Why had she chosen me to ter-rorize? Perhaps Maria really liked me more than the others, and I had never noticed. I would try to notice in the future.

But nothing about Maria seemed to have changed. She was nice to everyone. Especially now, with elections coming on, she was very nice to everyone. If she gave me a quick hug, or put her arm around me, or favored me with a smile, it was a moment of excitement and joy for me, but the hug or the smile was soon given to someone else. Everyone loved her. She was the star. She could not fail.

When the day came in Assembly for nominating speeches, even the frightened little girls who had never spoken in Assembly before were timorously waving their hands. There was a greater variety of campaign statements than ever before. Instead of the gulped "She's uh . . . good," or "She's been here a long time," which were repeated only three or four times for Maria, people actually made speeches about how exceptional she was. We were all happy and a little proud. It was to be a secret write-in ballot because we were a democracy, but we supposed Maria would win almost unanimously. She seemed to have won already. When she smiled at us, her smile said not only Please, but Thank you. She looked very beautiful, dignified, even radiant. Distant. She had never loved me, Kathlyn's jealousy notwithstanding, and she never would. I was just another one of her people.

And then I knew what I had to do.

At the time I knew only that I loved her so much and so unrequitedly that I had to hurt her, but for years afterward I wondered why I had done it, and later I supposed it was because love —unless it is really true love—is very close to hate. Certainly in adolescence, when emotions are new and fierce and unfamiliar, even unwelcome, love and hate are intermixed. I think, most of all, I wanted to . . . I *had to* . . . make Maria be more like me, bring her down to my level because I knew I could never reach her on hers.

At any rate, I did not vote for Maria for president. And when the write-in ballots were finally counted, it was discovered that many other girls had not voted for Maria, perhaps because they loved her too, like me, and so, to everyone's shock, it was very close but she lost. The girl who won looked dazed. When the results were announced, Maria's normally pale skin went bright red, and she jumped up from her seat in the auditorium and ran out.

The girls were nearly hysterical. They had a

quick second election for president of the student council, and that one went to Maria as a consolation and the only sensible, decent thing to do, but she was not there to hear it. I could scarcely wait for the meeting to be adjourned, and as soon as it was, I broke from the line and disappeared. I knew what I was going to find, and some instinct led me to exactly the place where I would find it.

Upstairs, on an empty floor, in one of the empty classrooms, the one my animal instinct led me to directly . . . there I found her. First I heard the sound, very soft, through the half-closed door, of someone sobbing. I tiptoed to the door and quietly looked in. Maria did not see me. She was sitting on the window sill, bathed in late afternoon light, her thin hands over her face, her whole body shaking, sobbing in pain and grief and shock and disappointment, weeping for the death of a dream she had had for the past ten years. Her long dark hair streamed around her face, and when she took her hands away for a moment to search again for her mangled handkerchief, I saw her face gleaming with tears . . . tears . . . tears. I thought I should say something polite like "I'm sorry you lost the election," but I did not want to, and so I spied on her and said nothing. I watched her cry and I felt a deep, nasty sense of pleasure and power. For the first time I really loved her. She was weak and I was strong, and I was happy. You're mine, I thought. At last you're mine. You're hurt and you lost and I'm glad. I love you. You're mine.

When I stole out of the room, Pam was waiting for me in the hall. "Isn't it terrible . . ." she began, and then stopped, looking at my face. She looked at me in shock, then suspicion. "You did vote for her, didn't you?" she said.

"It's a secret ballot," I said.

Pam's eyes were very dark and flat. "You *did* vote for her? You've got to tell me!"

"Did you?"

"Of course!" she said. "Did you? You've got to tell me."

"I'll never tell you," I said, suddenly nervous.

"If you don't tell me, I'll never be your friend again."

I knew she meant it. But I knew that she knew the truth anyway, and that she would never be my friend again anyway.

"No," I said, "I didn't."

Pam gasped. "How could you?"

Kathlyn was standing there listening to it all,

glaring at me as if I were a murderess. She turned without a word and put her arm around Pam's waist, and Pam put her arm around Kathlyn's waist, and the two of them walked away together. Neither of them ever spoke to me again.

The next day at Assembly the result of the election for president of the student council was announced again so Maria could hear it, and everyone applauded with genuine feeling and friendliness, and Maria smiled graciously and nodded thank you, so it almost seemed as if she had won a victory. Everyone was so sorry for her and liked her so much that it did seem as if this were her victory. She was no longer Romeo; she was just Juliet like the rest of us, young and vulnerable. She seemed thinner, more slight to me, more human. For the first time I noticed that she wasn't so beautiful, just a very striking seventeen-year-old girl, and I knew that some day we would both grow up and it wouldn't make so much difference that she was five years older than I and had once been the heroine of a hundred girls.

Sometimes I saw Pam and Kathlyn walking together to the drugstore. They were always deep in conversation, and I would wonder if they were still talking about how much they loved Maria. I wondered why they didn't grow up. They always snubbed me. Till the end of their days they would always think I had done a vicious and a dishonorable thing.

Perhaps I did . . . but is it not the first prerogative of a free adult to choose freely and choose what he believes? It is—but I could not choose what I believed, and so what I did was a vicious and a dishonorable thing. I knew Maria would make a wonderful president. There was no reason why she wouldn't. She had poise, she knew what to do, and she loved the school more than most of us ever could. The school had always been her home. She had always believed in it. And she would never understand why the school had somehow betrayed her. As for me, I hated the school with all my heart, and I hated most of the girls. I hated at least half the teachers, one of whom I hated so much that every night I wished her dead. I liked a few of the teachers because they put up with me and actually treated me as if my opinions mattered. But they were not the school to me; to me the school was a huge, ugly, uniformed body of girls who thought they knew everything because they had grown up together. They didn't know a thing. They didn't know about love being like hate.

They didn't know about me. They didn't know what I had done, nor why I had done it.

But perhaps . . . they did understand. After all, Maria had lost. My love, that wanted to hurt what it could not possess, was perhaps not unique after all. Perhaps most of them were just jealous of her because she had a poise and popularity and talent they could never have. Or perhaps, like me, they loved her too, too much, and knew the only way they could win her was to hurt her first. Adolescence is an island . . . there are no rules. Whatever we learn, we have to fight it out alone.

As I look back at what I have written here, it seems to me that this first year of my adolescence was empty, emotionless, full of protracted excitement about petty things. But it was also the first year of my real life, and so I was just beginning to find out what feelings were. I do not know how it was for other girls at this time, whether they were so choked with feelings that they paraded as little ladies, or whether they, too, were resting, trying to sort things out, and so the sap flowed slower. I think the pain and bewilderment of my childhood, which protected itself by detachment, was replaced in adolescence by a much realer detachment, the

detachment of the novice, the tentative experi-
menter. The hours we spent waiting outside Maria's
apartment building or wandering on the streets discussing a subject until it was chewed dry were necessary, for we had no way of feeling love, and so we
had to talk about it. We talked and talked until
we made ourselves believe that we could feel. So
it was, and so it had to be for a few more years.
It could not be otherwise. The heart had to grow
to catch up with the mind. Grownups say it is
the other way around with teen-agers. But they are
wrong. They have merely forgotten.

4

O I Love You
Adolph Green

In the course of growing up, I think there is one truly happy time in every girl's life: the time between her unrequited crushes on unattainable older girls and her unrequited infatuations with elusive older boys. That is the time when she is safely, if dramatically, in love with The Star.

If psychiatrists were to go back and pinpoint the exact time when a neurotic woman stopped growing emotionally, I suspect Freud would often be proved wrong. I do not think it was the time her father "deserted" her when she was five or seven, or the time her prettier younger sister was born when she was nine. I think it was the happy, safe, fulfilled, undemanding year when she was settling into adolescence and was in love with The Star. Perhaps that would account for the number of girls who waste their lives pursuing married men or falling in love with their bosses. I don't think these girls are looking for their fathers. I think they are looking for that long-ago year when life was full of love, and love could not hurt but only tantalize. But of course I'm not a doctor, and so I can only tell about me.

I was thirteen and in my second year of high school. My love for Maria seemed long in the past, and my passions for college boys seemed far in the future. I looked like any other ordinary dreadful adolescent in the 1940's—I was five feet two and a half, I weighed 111 pounds, I wore braces and purple-red lipstick, I had a few blemishes which I covered carefully with a death mask of pancake make-up (the kind you wet with a sponge and that came only in a sort of orange color in those days), I had shoulder length hair with bangs, which I set incessantly so that the bangs turned up at the ends, and I still did not shave my legs because I thought girls who did that were not nice. I owned the same pair of shoes with Cuban heels, but I did not have stockings. Rather, my mother had bought me several pairs of what mothers bought daughters in those days when the daughters refused to wear socks: nylon things that looked like stockings but ended just above the ankle. I wore these with my Cuban heel shoes for dress-up.

Because we wore school uniforms all day, I did not own many clothes, but I did have a navy blue rayon-crepe dress with shoulder pads, which was also for dress-up, as distinguished from my yellow rabbit's hair and gold sequin dress, which was for school dances. The navy dress, with the transparent nylon socks and the brown Cuban-heeled shoes, from which my legs emerged hairy, white, and red-kneed on cold days, was for Saturday afternoons. On these occasions I filched my mother's fur jacket, which was brown squirrel with shoulder pads and must have been rather disreputable or she would never have allowed me to wander around in it.

In short, I thought I looked beautiful, but I was a spectacle.

I was still receiving a dollar fifty a week allowance, which was still to be used for bus fare to the dentist and then for such luxuries as drugstore sundaes and the movies. But now I used it for the theater. I was suddenly madly stage struck.

Someone had given me an autograph book, as people always do when you are thirteen, but I considered myself too sophisticated to use it. The closest I ever came to the barbaric custom of getting autographs was when I persuaded Skippy Homeier, who was fascinating us all as the child Nazi in *Tomorrow the World,* to autograph one of my girlfriend's white saddle shoes. For myself, if any kind actress saw me in a crowd of autograph seekers and asked me if I would like an autograph too, I would reply politely, "No, thank you." I thought that was dignified and kind, although I suppose I must have hurt some people's feelings because they thought I didn't like them. I did like them, but I thought not bothering them was the way to show it.

Saturday afternoons I always went to a matinee. Standing room cost a dollar fifty, and I appeared so many times at the same show that the usherettes knew me and allowed me to sit in any empty seat if there was one, or if not, I could sit on the floor of the aisle on my mother's squirrel jacket. I was already well versed in the intricacies of show business, which meant I knew how to sneak in to a show free for the second act by mingling with the audience when they came out for intermission and then simply going back in with them. The ratio of second acts I saw versus entire shows ranged at least four to one.

I usually took an accomplice. The other girls were afraid at first, but I approached this second-act watching with such an air of It Is My Right that their fears were soon calmed. It did not occur to me that any usherette could possibly eject a child who had such a love of the theater as I had—and none of them ever did.

Unlike the older girls in our school, I did not date boys, because I did not know any except one boy from my grade school days in Brooklyn. He used to telephone me and then sit there whistling self-consciously because he could not think of anything to say. I would whistle too, and thus we would have our courtship. He had neither the courage nor the allowance to take me anywhere, for which I was just as glad. I would not have had the courage to go out with him and whistle the entire evening.

My grand passion began the night my parents took me to see *On the Town*. It was the most exciting musical I have ever seen in my life. I will never know if I would think so today, but I thought so then, and that's the way I remember it. The show was about New York. The moment the curtain rose on the breathtaking set of the Brooklyn Bridge and the Navy Yard I knew that forevermore the theater would be the greatest passion of my life. Then the three sailors came out and sang "New York, New York, it's a helluva town . . ." I knew just how they felt. New York was an adventure to me, an afterschool adventure, when I, too, was allowed out on leave.

There was a tall, handsome blond sailor, a tall, dark, winsome sailor, and a little funny one. I fell madly in love with the little funny one. Why should I not love him, for he was me! His name was Adolph Green.

He had a slightly simian appearance, a rubber face, and energy. He always got into scrapes. He was kinetic, lovable, and a loser. I thought he was the sexiest man in the world.

He and Betty Comden had written the show, which made him more than a Star; he was also a genius. I memorized all the lyrics. I discovered legends about him, such as the story that he used to walk all the way from Brooklyn to the Bronx reading a book the entire way and never getting clipped by a car. He was twenty-seven, which to me was the most perfect and sexiest age in the world (if he had been twenty-one or forty-five, I would have felt the same way), and he was not married. It did not matter much to me whether he was married or not, because although I dreamed of marrying him, I knew I was thirteen years old. However, I liked the idea that he was single, because it fit in better with my daydreams.

In the Eighty-sixth Street subway station there was a machine where you could put in a quarter and stamp out twenty-five letters on a round tin medallion about the size of a quarter. I went to this machine and made a medal which said, o i LOVE YOU ADOLPH GREEN. It was spelled "O" and not "Oh" because I thought this more poetic. I carried this medal in my wallet through all the years of high school. When we were graduated and other girls had things written about them in the Yearbook like "That beautiful blond hair" or "A friend to all and a natural leader," mine said, "Betty and Adolph."

I also discovered that my aunt and Betty Comden's aunt had been friends in Brooklyn. I nagged my aunt until she arranged for me to interview Betty for the high school newspaper.

The interview was titled "Stardust and Grease-paint." It was possibly the dullest interview ever written, for I felt I was writing about someone who was a cross between Albert Schweitzer and Sarah Bernhardt, so I confined the piece to a biography anyone could have gotten from the theater pages of a newspaper. The things that really fascinated me backstage—the false eyelashes that Betty removed in front of me when all the time I had thought they were real, the funny things people said in the dressing room, the feeling of being backstage that fascinated me and would have fascinated any teen-ager—were omitted out of terror. The only thing about the printed interview that was interesting was that the printer made a mistake and captioned her photograph BETTY CONDOM, which none of us were old enough to notice until the Editor-in-Chief of the paper, who was a senior, noticed it and had all the issues pulled and corrected.

The other interesting thing about the interview was that from then on the backstage doorman recognized me as some little friend of Betty's and let me come in whenever I wanted to. When I wanted to was every Saturday matinee.

I made myself fairly invisible, despite my weird attire and make-up, and everybody grew used to me. Once I was even allowed to watch the show from the wings. All I wanted was to stay backstage at *On the Town* for the rest of my life.

One day I went into Betty's dressing room and there was a knock at the door. I went behind the door and stood there. The door opened and in walked Adolph. I sprang out from behind the door, like someone in a spy film, and gasped, "Oh, I love you, Adolph Green!"

He did a double take and looked terrified, said what he had come to say to Betty (glancing furtively at me in case I meant to do something more dramatic), and beat a hasty retreat. I told all the girls at school about it, and they thought I was brave and that the incident had been very romantic.

After I had been to see the show seven or eight times, three entire times and five second acts, to be exact, I felt it was time to display my show business sophistication and bring a friend. I took one of the girls in my class, a follower, who was very frightened. I clutched her firmly by the arm, and we sneaked in to the second act. Then I took her backstage. By then the doorman was saying hello to me, as were some of the cast. We stood in the corner and watched everybody leaving, saw the little kids asking for autographs, breathed the

frankincense of dancers' perspiration, and felt superior. It was a lovely afternoon, and I wanted
nothing more of life.

It never occurred to me to telephone Adolph
Green and bother him, or giggle, or whatever girls
that age do on the phone with Star strangers, because to me he had no life outside of that magic
stage and our chance encounters in the wings. Of
course I had his picture on my bulletin board, and
of course I kissed it goodnight every night. I never
thought of touching him. My medal that said O I
LOVE YOU ADOLPH GREEN was my touchstone, my
lucky charm, my pacifier. I never thought of showing it to him. I looked at it often, and fingered the
raised letters, and felt happy.

When other girls asked me why I didn't love
someone like Frank Sinatra or William Holden, I
thought they were daft. Who could possibly have
a crush on Frank Sinatra? Now Adolph Green . . .
there was a sex symbol. He wasn't some singing
star whom women fainted over at the Paramount;
he was my own personal private passion. As for the
boys from prep schools, whom we were forced to
dance with and whom some of us even kissed
when people put out the lights at parties, they were
unthinkable to me. They had sweaty palms, talked

about how their sunburn had peeled last summer, and if you danced cheek to cheek, you might catch their acne. Who wanted them? Who needed them? Not I.

Eventually *On the Town* closed a long successful run, and Betty and Adolph went to Hollywood, and I grew up and went to college to be confronted by life. And years later, when I was grown up and a writer, old enough so that everyone at a party could be equal no matter what their age, I met Adolph Green again. I told him about the medal, and he seemed incredulous and then rather delighted. I told him I would give it to him, but like so many things of the past I could never find it.

He has been married for quite a few years now —to a young woman my age—and that's as it should be when people are grown up. I wonder if someday I will marry someone with whom a thirteen-year-old girl was madly in love when he was twenty-seven. I am sure that if I do, he won't even remember her. And that is how it should be, too, for great loves like that should be of importance only to the little girl.

I hope Big Stars will always be kind to little girls who love them, standing against backstage alley walls or even inside a dressing room if they are lucky, dressed in their funny too-grown-up clothes, clutching their Playbills or their cameras. Not too kind, for a word or a smile is enough. The little girl will dream about it for weeks afterward. And so she has this island of perfect love in the middle of the most turbulent years of growing up. It is all totally unrealistic, and yet . . . she is going to go through so much later on. She needs that peace. It is as if life decided to give her a short vacation.

5

Rose White
and Rose Red

We are the behemoths—lost, lumbering, out of our time. We are about to become extinct. And yet we are young, barely thirty, and we have not even begun to live. When we were children and our parents and their friends were the grownups—slightly ridiculous and painfully aware of it, so it made them stricter, shriller, quicker to anger—we were small and afraid. Now the children, the teen-agers, are tall and sure, cool, good at talk and flirting, able to keep silence without blushing and writhing, able to look one in the eye and be amused. I suppose they must be fright-

ened, too, but not as frightened as we were, because they speak and sing to each other and tell all
the world when grownups lie. We never admitted
lies, to ourselves or to our friends, although day by
day the terrified about-to-become-extinct grownups
lied to us, weaving their fabric of myth as tightly
as they could, believing it would be our coat of
mail against a hostile world their own parents had
not been able to understand. They swaddled us,
saying proudly all the same that swaddling was
barbaric. They bound our hearts, telling us at the
same time of the ancient Chinese who bound their
daughters' feet so they could not run to the men
they loved. And can we run now, with bound
hearts, with frightened eyes, with arms tightly
clutched to our sides in coats of mail that were
supposed to protect that flower that bloomed within
us, which no one had ever seen and which one
could only believe, blindly, ever existed at all?

The other day I was in a taxi stopped at a red
light, and I saw a group of teen-agers, none of
them older than fourteen, grouped on the corner.
They were on their way home from school, and I
recognized one of them as the daughter of one of
my friends, who had married when she was seventeen. This child was now taller than her mother,

and beautiful, and she was obviously the girl all the boys liked the best. They clustered around her, teasing and flirting, and she swung her long hair and dealt with them with a bemused poise and nonchalance that it took us twenty years to achieve. I thought of her mother, divorced and bewildered, reading her paperback psychology books and never finding the answers to the men who complicated her life . . . and then I looked at the child, who seemed to know by instinct when life need not be complicated. The child had never been lied to, for we had learned that much, although painfully. She could never teach her mother, for a mother is still a mother, even when she is as reckless and lost as a child. The children blame us for being fools, but for being different kinds of fools than our parents were, and they are right. But in one respect they are wrong—for we want desperately to live, even when it seems almost too late, while our parents did not know how to live, and so they gave up. My mother says, looking into the mirror, "Oh, I'm an old thing," just as we say it without a mirror. There is the same tone of loss and regret in her voice as we have in ours, and yet we are barely thirty, and she and her friends are in their sixties and even their fifties. The children, the fourteen-year-olds, are older than we are. But they will know how to live. They are grown up. We are only old.

So this is how it happened, the thing we all feared, and it happened so quickly we never knew until it was too late. There was childhood and anxiety and bewilderment, and then suddenly we were the older generation, not much smarter, still frightened, a little wiser. What happened to the time between, when we were supposed to be those sleek happy adults who did all the sophisticated things we dreamed of when we were adolescents and college girls? What happened to being grown up?

Perhaps it is happening to us now and we do not know it, and so this is all there is. Perhaps those teen-agers flirting on the corner saw me in the taxi and thought I was one of Them, the sleek grownups, on my way to something exciting and mysterious that they would someday find too. A cocktail party? A dinner? A lover? Aren't these the things we dreamed about when we were young, the things we read about in books, the things our mothers told us were dangerous? And how boring they are! No one ever told us they would be boring. Did no one know, or would no one admit it, or did the grownups then think that for us it would be different, more exciting, more dangerous, just as today we think it must be for the children just beginning?

When I was sixteen, I entered college, and I knew several things. One: I would eventually receive my first kiss on the mouth, and it would have to be from a boy I loved. Two: I would be torn at by dirty fingers in the front or back seat of cars, and I would tear them away and remain clean. Three: I would try my best to get married before I graduated, because otherwise no one would ever marry me, because there were no boys back home, while there were hundreds of them at college, all available. Four: If I did not marry, I would remain a virgin until I was twenty-one, because twenty-one was the age of wisdom and consent. Five: Everybody was a virgin, except for certain boys who had been treated to trips to Europe during the summer holidays and had done it with a French whore. Six: After I graduated, if I was unmarried, when I reached the age of twenty-one and had had my first lover, I would then have

fifty lovers, write their names down on a private
piece of paper, and after that I would give up sex
completely and relax in the knowledge that I had
not been entirely undesirable and that I had lived
a full life.

From this list it is obvious that the wholesome
precepts we had been taught in the 40's about
Rose White vs. Rose Red put so much emphasis
on pure, clean Real Love that they blotted love
entirely out of our comprehension. The kids today
may be cool, but they are not half so cool as we
were. We knew the value of a bargain. The bargain, and its value, was to be on our terms. We
were to talk a great deal about love in the years
that followed, especially if we were being immoral
and conscience-stricken, but we would not have
more than the slightest idea what love was.

This is what happened to my list:

1) My first kiss on the mouth was from a boy I
detested, who was the president of his college
fraternity, looked like Groucho Marx (without the
mustache), and who had obviously never kissed a
girl before, although I was not to realize that until
several years later. The boy I was really in love
with did not get up the nerve to kiss me until

Christmas vacation, a kiss I cherished for months, and he (I found out ten years later) was having a homosexual affair with both his roommates.

2) I will avoid any discussion of the dirty fingers because I am too embarrassed.

3) The only man who proposed to me while I was at college was an assistant professor and much too old for me. Besides, he told me that if we got married, he would expect to cheat and that I could do the same, but that this would in no way affect the quality of our devotion to each other. I disagreed. He introduced me to his parents, who turned out to be like two little wrens and not at all what I would have expected to be the parents of a twenty-seven-year-old lecher who advocated infidelity before he was even engaged. I did not marry him.

4) I remained a virgin according to plan.

5) Most of the boys I dated had, indeed, been virgins until that trip to Europe and the legendary French whore, or at least they told me so, but here begins my story. It is sad, I think, because it concerns two vulnerable, confused human beings—myself and the boy who was my best friend at college—and because in a way we loved each other, although neither of us was prepared in any way to

understand that, for love was many different things
to both of us, none of them warmth and communication and security and laughter, the things we had
together. We thought we loved only other people,
people we did not understand and whom we even
rather hated from our confusion of feelings.

I was eighteen and a junior. He was a senior,
but he was about twenty-four and had been in the
CIA. I think we met in Shakespeare class, one of
the most boring classes of all because it involved
memorizing all the punctuation of a speech down
to the last semicolon, and if you got more than
four commas or semicolons wrong—never mind
any actual words—you would flunk the test. The
professor who gave the class later committed suicide. My friend, whom I will call David because
that is not his name, was very tall and thin, and he
liked only thin girls, the thinner the better. He
told me years later that he was always looking for
a girl thinner than himself because he thought he
was ugly, but at the time I knew only that I was
fat and unattractive. He told me once, "You have
the kind of figure that would be a Miss America,
which most men like, but I just happen to like
them skinny and flat chested." I knew perfectly
well that no one in his right mind would ever want

me to be Miss America, but I never considered
dieting because he was not really my type, either,
and the fact that we were not attracted to each
other made our deep affection much more un-
complicated.

He took me to dinner every other night and
often telephoned me between times just to talk, or
dropped by my dormitory to see me. The other
girls, except for my closest friends, assumed he was
my boyfriend, and they thought I was lucky because he was sophisticated and intelligent and
funny. Actually, we were both in love with other
people.

The girl David thought he loved would have
nothing to do with him, which was, I think, why
he loved her, for she was not at all skinny and she
never moved her lips when she talked. She smoked
a lot, I remember, and was quite pretty in a
locked-in sort of way. Most of our dinners together
were spent with David telling me how much he
loved this girl and how she had seemed a little
kinder the night before or had perhaps spoken a
little more warmly to him that morning in class. I
was jealous and bored, but I was flattered that he
wanted to confide in me, and so I pretended to be
very interested in every detail of this nonromance.

Finally, one evening as I was gorging myself at the glamorous grown-up restaurant where he had taken me, David said (more out of conscience than interest), "I'm always talking about myself. You never talk about you. There must be somebody *you* like."

Was there? I did like someone, but he hardly knew I was alive, and besides, I had been brought up to know that girls bored boys by talking about themselves. I said there was someone, but that I didn't want to discuss it. He insisted. Finally I confessed. Well . . . there was this boy . . . he looked like Heathcliff . . . very dark and poetic, long hair, kind of funny clothes, ascots and things . . . a sad childhood . . . sensitive and shy . . . and he didn't take out any of the girls from school, just once in a while some prep school blonde who arrived in Harvard Square with a baby-blue suitcase. As a matter of fact, I was madly in love with this Heathcliff, as were several other girls, but he was so hard to get. At last David and I could suffer together. It was such a rewarding feeling that I think I embellished my romance just to please him, and my crush from afar became the grand passion of my life, at least during my dinners with David.

During that winter I had only one date with

Heathcliff, if you could call it a date. He wandered by my dormitory, found me there almost by accident, and we went into the little room where they kept the Coke machine. We sat on the floor next to the Coke machine, he with his coat on, and he told me that he was very unhappy all the time, but he would not tell me why. He seemed to be about to cry. I tried to think of something understanding and womanly to say. I said, "Go ahead and cry; it will make you feel better. Go on. I don't mind."

His face got darker, as if everything inside him was twisting, and then he managed to spill a few tears, but not enough to make anyone feel better, only enough to embarrass him so much that he ran out into the snow and never came to see me again.

Years later I found out that he was another one of the group of Harvard homosexuals, and I suppose it was that which was making him so unhappy. I seemed to have a talent for meeting secret homosexuals at school (all of whom intended to reform as soon as they were graduated, and none of whom did) because I was so innocent and militantly virginal that none of them were afraid of me. Anyway, the other girls were impressed that Heathcliff had come to see me at all, for I was the only girl who had never knitted him a school scarf (I couldn't knit) or sent him a note or gone to his dormitory on some flimsy pretext. I wrote my mother a long letter in which I said that Heathcliff didn't know I was alive, and that I loved him, and that I was obviously worthless, and she wrote back that *she* loved me.

David couldn't figure out what was the matter with Heathcliff when I told him about the stingy tears at the Coke machine, but at least I had something to report. And then I introduced David to his real love.

She was the thinnest girl in the entire school, absolutely straight, with a body like an arm. He saw her across the living room at the dorm and asked me to introduce him to her. I was his friend, so I obliged. They made a date for that night. I must have been so jealous that I completely put it out of my mind that I had brought them together, for I never remembered it until years later when he told me. I had always supposed he had just discovered her somewhere.

How can I describe her? She was cool, blondish, quiet, dressed in tweeds and cashmeres, came from an intellectual family, had gone to a fashionable boarding school, came from the Midwest, was, as

I said, terribly thin and bosomless, and looked just like what my mother would have thought was a Rose White. On their first date she insisted that David make love to her, which he did—flattered beyond words—and then she told him she was in love with him. Naturally I was fascinated and asked all sorts of stupid questions.

Where did you go to do it? They were building a new dormitory on the Quadrangle, and inside the partly finished building, which had rows of cement-floored future bedrooms and was deserted at night, was a beehive of illicit sexual activity; all the teen-agers in that shell of a building acting their shells of make-believe love. Since I couldn't imagine anyone lying on a cement floor in the winter, I assumed they had done it standing up, with their coats on, so I didn't ask him about that.

How come she didn't get pregnant? David was embarrassed at that, but he mumbled that he had managed to take care of things, leaving me to my futile imagination.

Anyway, she was now his girl, and they were in love. Or at least, she was in love with him, and he found her body irresistible and her love for him wonderful. He planned to take her away for a whole weekend.

During the previous summer he had been a counselor at a boys' camp, and the camp was now deserted, rustic and beautiful with snow-covered trees and, best of all, cabins with beds. It was not difficult to get away from college for a weekend if you were not afraid; all you had to do was write in the sign-out book the name and address of a fictitious relative whom you were going to visit. For me, it would have been incomprehensible, the most frightening thing in the world, but David's girl was very calm about it and actually wrote the name of a real relative, an uncle in New York. They returned on Sunday night in time for supper; he went back to his dormitory, and I found myself sitting next to Rose Red alone at a table in the dining room. I kept staring at her, wondering why she didn't look guilty or different. She was calm and talked to me about various things, none of them the weekend that had just happened. I don't know if she knew or not that I knew about it. I remember it was late, and there was nothing left to eat but a big bowl of potato salad with wilted lettuce, but she ate heartily while I mangled my lettuce with my fork and kept wondering why she hadn't changed. Were there other girls like her, who slept with boys and still looked just like everybody else? Could I ever do it? I knew I could never have that pleasant charm that seemed to suffuse her; she wasn't embarrassed at all. Everything she said to me seemed earthy and significant, although all I remember was that she told me she used to blush when she had to go to the bathroom.

David took me to dinner again a night or two later and told me the weekend was fine. Then he said, reluctant and a little embarrassed, "Look . . . you've always been my best friend, but now that I'm in love with her . . . well, she ought to be my best friend. I mean, the girl I'm in love with has to be my best friend, right? It wouldn't do if you were my best friend any more. I mean, you and I will still see each other, but we can't confide in each other the way we used to, because now I've got to confide everything to her."

I said that was all right, I understood. I did understand. I was sorry, but not surprised, for I knew that love had to encompass friendship as well, and besides, now that he had a girl who loved him, he would have nothing to confide. I supposed there were things they would tell each other—deep, adult things that I was not yet to be privileged to know—and I wondered what they were and felt sad. But love was everything . . .

we all knew that . . . and in a way I was relieved not to have to make up lies about my love for Heathcliff any more because it had always been David whom I cared about, even though in an entirely different way. I was glad he had found a girl who loved him, and although I had been thoroughly indoctrinated with the idea that a man would never love a girl he had "ruined," I knew she had long since been "ruined" by somebody else and that David didn't mind at all. I knew he was a grownup because he was older than any of us, and because he had always talked to me like a grownup, and I knew I was a child and too fat for him. It seemed simple. The only thing I could not understand was how Rose Red could still seem so calm.

In the spring, when David was about to be graduated, they became engaged. All the girls admired Rose Red's little antique diamond ring, which was the biggest and prettiest diamond any of the engaged girls at school had ever had. The wedding was planned for the summer, back in her home town in the Midwest, and she would either quit college altogether or finish wherever David's work took him. Although he and I were still friends, I hardly ever saw him, and whenever I did, he seemed almost a stranger to me. Even when I saw him, I missed him, and I knew that when he graduated, I would never see him again. He seemed to miss me, too. He was very tender with me, as if he hoped something good would happen to me before he went away so that he would not have to worry about my life. He was the only boy who knew how shy I really was; all the ones I dated were so insecure that I had them completely fooled.

My last year at college was coming, and I had things to worry about. I had to find that husband or fiancé before it was too late, and walking to classes through Harvard Yard, looking at all the boys who seemed so handsome and sexy and worthy of my lifelong love, I wondered how I could ever get one of them to want me. Any of them—it didn't matter. Each one I looked at seemed wonderful, even the worst ones had redeeming qualities. I felt that I was so worthless that to capture any one of them would give me peace, status, and happiness forever. I looked at the girls who went steady, some of them even engaged, all of them so casual and carefree in the love that surrounded them that they could rush out to meet their special man every night dressed in jeans and a wrinkled boy's shirt and sneakers, without even bothering to put on lipstick because they knew it would all be kissed off anyway by one o'clock curfew.

A few of the girls had gotten married, and one or two of them were so pregnant by the time they had to take their spring final exams that they could not fit behind the little desks. There was a great rush to have the first class baby, who would forevermore be the official class mascot. The married girls lived in apartments or off-campus houses with their husbands, except for one girl, whose husband was in the Army. I remember there was a great quandary about what to do with her . . . after all, she was a Married Woman, and therefore capable of corrupting the rest of us (according to the authorities), but since her husband was away, they couldn't send the poor thing out of the dorm to live alone. It was finally decided to let her continue to live in the dorm. She was one of the sweetest, most beautiful girls I had ever seen, very fragile and gentle. She had married her childhood sweetheart, a boy who looked like the college hero of those wholesome family movies we had seen in high school. Whenever he got an evening pass, they would run off together into the darkness, to go . . . who knows where? Where was there to go for two kids with no money and no home, with nothing but a marriage license and love? She always had to sign in with the rest of us at 1 A.M. Sometimes her husband had a weekend pass, and then she would sign out in the book to his family's address. I remember always feeling happy for her then, and hoping that his family had a very, very large house on a deserted windswept beach.

I wonder who there was left to corrupt. Me, of course. And one girl, a freshman, who necked with every boy she went out with until she became so popular and notorious that the boys who called for blind dates did not give her their real names. When she was not necking, she was absent-mindedly gobbling up all the food at the dormitory table or wandering around the dining room tearing at the soft centers of muffins with her fingers. She was expelled for bad marks. And there was the other freshman, the one who thought no one else in the world but herself bled every month, and that it was a horrible affliction she must never admit to anyone. She left school to have a nervous breakdown. And there was the girl, a year ahead of me, who stopped going to morning classes and wandered around the upper hall in a man's silk

foulard bathrobe, pale with morning sickness.
When she left college to marry the boy, only a
few months short of her diploma, she explained
graphically and technically to her girlfriends how
it had actually been an Immaculate Conception.
Since her description was so ingenious, we all believed her and felt sorry for her at having such
bad luck. We felt it was really a dangerous world
where you got punished for doing nothing.

No one would corrupt me. No one would tell
me anything. No one would tell anyone anything.

And so I graduated, and armed with my Rad-
cliffe-Harvard diploma, which told me I was now
an educated woman, I went home to live with my
parents.

When it actually happened is not clear in my
mind; I remember only the morning itself when
the wedding invitation arrived in the mail, and
taking it to read alone in my room, sitting on the
blue bedspread reading and rereading that invitation, I was sure that some monstrous misprint had
changed David's last name. It was the engraved
invitation to the wedding of Miss Rose Red to Mr.
David Somebody Else. She had never been my
special friend; he had been, and so naturally I had

received this invitation, for who but a special friend would be invited to journey all the way to the Midwest for a wedding with no plane ticket enclosed? In those days I still believed everything: A wedding invitation was an *invitation,* not a convenient announcement. For a few days I actually considered making the trip, partly because I was flattered (I had been invited to few weddings so far in my life), and partly to see for myself if it was a misprint or someone else she was marrying.

I finally decided against going, but for months the memorized name of Mr. David Somebody Else stumbled in my head, until I felt disassociated from reality. From the real David I heard nothing.

He was in New York, and I was in New York, but once back in the home of my childhood the fears and shyness of my childhood overcame me as if I had never left, and so for two years I never saw anyone from college again. I found a job in a company that published paperback originals; I read manuscripts; I learned to converse, flirt, and drink with grownups, to stay out overnight and lie to my parents, to keep true to the lie even through my mother's insistent cross-examining, to fear the world outside, and even more to fear the world at home. I learned to drive a car, to use dirty words without blushing, and again to contemplate suicide. I dated a succession of Nice Eligible Young Men (lawyers) and Catches (doctors) and Young Men Who Might Have a Nice Friend (textile magnates). They all terrified me. I went to a million night clubs, danced a million dances, drank a million whiskey sours, had my hair done a half-million times, and stared out of my bedroom window and my office window for hours, thinking of nothing. I envied the unmarried girls at my office who had their own apartments or lived with another girl, who were allowed to entertain, to cook, to do what they wanted. My mother read the Sunday *Times* and saw the Catches slipping away.

"You could have had him," she would say, as the photograph of a martinet-faced, waved-haired rich girl would appear over the announcement that another of my young doctors had been taken.

"I didn't ever want him," I would say, "and he didn't want me."

My mother always ignored this. "You could have had him," she would repeat, "if you had tried."

I began seeing some of the boys from college.

Now they were living in hives together, the ex-roommates, roommates again in New York while they made a career.

"They won't be your lasting friends," she would say.

I looked up David in the phone book and wrote him a letter. "Are you rich, are you famous?" I asked him. I told him of the stories I had written that had finally been published in magazines. When we had been in college together, the literary magazine, of which he was the editor-in-chief, had always rejected my stories and poetry. I had never been upset by what I considered their pretentious intolerance. I knew that when I grew up, I would continue to write, and that I would write a novel, and everyone would love it, and everyone would finally love me. I had told him that, and he had laughed.

By mistake I sent the letter to David's father. David was out of the country, and he received the letter months later. He never answered it. I figured that was a sign he was indeed rich and famous —and married. I was right about all three. At least, he was rich and he was married, and he was famous in his field.

Girls liked my stories. I was at a dance once, with a Catch, a young doctor, and a girl came up to me and told me rather shyly how much she had liked my latest story in a magazine. She turned to him. "You must be very proud of her," she said.

He looked down at me coldly. "I have never read any of her stories," he said, "and I never will."

Ambition fuses in a series of moments like that. I knew he was resentful, and I hated him for it. I will publish more stories, I thought, and become a much better writer, and *more* people will like me, and I will never have to go out with you again.

Another one of my Eligibles, who had hung around for years, liked to tell me, "You're just Marjorie Morningstar. You think you're going to be a writer, but you're not. You'll end up married and living in Scarsdale."

Suddenly from my college world, where marriage and suburbs and at least five children had seemed the height of satisfaction, I was living in a world where it was "just" marriage and the unhappy ending to a few years of grandiose pretentions to something more exciting. I was being reeducated. People said to me that of course when I married, I would stop writing, as if writing were a harmless little hobby I had taken up to appear interesting enough to find an educated husband. It was not that I would have no time to write if I married, for my friends who married all had maids, and nurses for their babies; it was that writing would be offensive to my husband. It would be too rebellious, like commuting from the suburbs to model lingerie for strange men in a department store.

Who were these people with these ideas? Where had they come from? They had always been there —it was just that four years away from home had allowed me to forget them.

During the day I went to my office, and at night and on weekends I wrote. I wrote and wrote and wrote and wrote. I rewrote. I tore up. I retyped. I cut. I rewrote. I threw it away. I wrote and saved my money and waited; I threw away rejection letters even though they were nice and encouraging, for they made me sick with rejection, and I wrote and had more stories published, and then I quit my job and stayed home and wrote all the time, and rewrote, and got nicer rejection letters. And then one day I was promised that if I handed in one hundred and fifty pages of a novel, I would get a contract. So I said, "I'm moving into my own apartment on September first. Give me one month to get it decorated, and then I'll start the book on October first." That was summer.

On September first I moved into my first own apartment, six years after I had graduated from college, with my mother standing on the sidewalk in front of the house where I had just signed the lease, crying and begging me, "Just give me more time, just a little more time."

A year later my first novel was published, and everywhere people appeared from my past to remind me that I had told them I would write a novel some day and that they had laughed when I told them . . . and I didn't remember ever telling any of them that at all.

People invited me to parties. I went . . . terrified, afraid they expected me to be interesting. At one of these parties I met David, with his wife. She seemed shy and nice. He had not married Rose Red, and the invitation had not contained a misprint after all. He and his wife had two children. He said I must come to their apartment for dinner soon. I said I would be delighted to. We did not see each other again for seven years.

Then, one morning, my phone rang. He never asked if it was me, and I never asked who it was;

we both simply started talking as if we were still in college and it was just one of our daily phone conversations, except that he went through an explanation of how complicated it had been to get my phone number. Except for those few words at that party seven years before, we had not spoken to each other for fourteen years.

We made a date to meet for lunch. I suppose he was curious; certainly I was. There were some things I wanted to find out, for we were both older now, and we could talk about the past as if it were an amusing story that had happened to someone else.

The restaurant where he suggested we meet was one I had seen three times in the movies and had been to twice. It was sophisticated, expensive, chic, and in a genteel way overwhelming. I supposed he ate there every day. (It turned out later he hardly ever went there but had suggested it because he thought it was where *I* went all the time.)

While I was dressing and making up my eyes with special care, it occurred to me that I had lost twenty pounds since we had been in college. I was now one of those thin girls he admired so much. I wondered if he would remember he admired them.

I realized he had been married for a long time, and I knew about some men who had been married for a long time, for I had dated them. I was a grownup now, with my own life. When you are both grownups, the older one is no longer the older one. It had been many years, and yet, it had been no time at all. I wondered if we would fall in love. I didn't particularly want to, but still, I had seen so many things that anything was possible; and when you think about a very special friend of your youth, when you were too young to understand your feelings, you wonder what will happen now that you are in control of your words and looks. Memory is sometimes stronger than the present, and you have to know; you have to wonder until you know.

I was wearing my hair short and had my coat collar up and was wearing big sunglasses, but he recognized me. I recognized him instantly. He looked exactly the same—perhaps ten pounds heavier, which was to the good.

Neither of us was shy or embarrassed. But we had a drink immediately, so perhaps we were.

As we filled each other in on the past, I felt like someone who has been away on a trip. A trip into life perhaps, and now I was back with my old friend, armed with my new polish and knowledge. I wanted to ask him what had happened to Rose Red, but he brought it up first.

"Remember that awful romance?"

It is a strange feeling to have someone answer every one of your unspoken questions, in order; but considering our close relationship, perhaps it was not so odd after all.

"I never loved her," he said. "I never even liked her. Actually, I couldn't stand her. But she kept talking about love and badgering me to get married, until finally just to keep out of an argument I seemed to have gotten engaged to her.

"I really liked you," he went on. "You were the one I cared about. But you were so shy . . . You were the shyest girl I ever met. You used to blush. Do you still blush?"

"No," I said, and blushed.

"With her it was just sex," he said. "We didn't have one single thing in common. There was nothing we agreed on. There was nothing we could talk about without an argument. But there was sex, and she insisted she loved me . . ."

"You always told me I was too fat."

"Oh, I always looked for the skinniest girl around because I was so skinny. It made me feel more equal. I never thought you were too fat. But who could make a pass at you? You were so shy."

I ordered another drink although we were looking at our main course, neither of us eating it.

"You were the kindest human being I have ever known," he said. "I don't think people realized how vulnerable you really were. Do they know it now?"

"Some," I said, suddenly feeling all the beautiful and good things a fulfilled woman is supposed to feel. I wished men would always sit beside me and tell me how kind and vulnerable I really was.

"But then you didn't marry her," I said. I told him about the wedding invitation and what I had imagined. He laughed at that.

"It's really a dreadful story," he began. "She had gone home to make plans for the wedding, and I realized that I couldn't go through with it, because I didn't love her and I didn't have anything in common with her and I just couldn't stand it. So I called her and told her to come back to New York because I had to talk to her. We met in Grand Central Station. She brought some relative with her—an aunt, I think—because she suspected something terrible was going to happen. There was a Schrafft's in Grand Central Station,

I remember, and we went there, she and the aunt and I, and there I told her I couldn't go through with the wedding.

"She dissolved into tears, and the aunt took her over, and they went right back home on the next train. We never even got out into daylight."

I pictured them as they must have been: the boy, not so old and sophisticated as he had seemed to us, the girl who was planning her trousseau, the aunt who was wise in the ways of junior heartbreak, acting out their drama in Schrafft's underground. It sounded like something from a J. D. Salinger story. I supposed he had not even had the sense to fortify her and the aunt with a brandy before his revelation.

We sent the food back barely picked at and ordered coffee with two kinds of brandy in it. The waiter put a tray of small wrapped hard candies on the table, and I began surreptitiously putting them one by one into my purse.

"Here," he said. "If you're going to do it, do it right," and he poured the entire contents into my purse and motioned the waiter over to refill the tray. I liked him for that because it wasn't the kind of restaurant where you dared do something like that, and they had similar candies prominently displayed in the front for sale. I began to remember more things about him that I had liked.

"And now?" I said. "You're married."

"It sounds like the kiss of death to say this, but you'd really like my wife. She's very shy, but when she finally likes you, she really *likes* you. I hope I'm not making you hate her by saying this, but you and my wife would get along together very well."

"And how many children . . . ?"

"Four," he said. He told me their names and ages. "And you? There must be someone you like?"

Echoes . . . echoes.

"Yes . . ." I had to force myself to begin, for confiding about temporary happiness always comes hard to me, as if giving it a name would make it disappear. But as I started to tell him, I suddenly felt proud, and I realized that for the first time in my life, although it was premature to hope, I was really falling in love. As I spoke to David, the man I was telling him about seemed to appear before us and sit down at the table. As much as I feared the confidence would make everything reveal itself to be a myth, like my Heathcliff of the old days, I felt stronger as I talked, and even as the bitter-sweet fear rested on my tongue, I knew I had joined the human race.

"We will meet," he said. "The four of us."

Wild bird, frightened eagle, I use you to console myself with others, to be as they. And you, in your own first fear of love, are you telling some girl you once knew that now you love me?

"Yes, we must do that," I said.

When we left the restaurant, he bought me a five-dollar jar of mustard because I had admired the jar it came in and said I would like to put a flower in it. He was happy, grand, and successful. He was kind. He was the only man all through these years who had noticed that I was kind. He had always liked me, and he had never intruded on my timidity. I liked him, and I felt warm. And I knew that now, when all things were possible because we were grownups, it was not possible that anything between the two of us could change.

A friend is a friend. That is all. That is all, but that is all you should want. We had lied to each other, but we would not lie now. He was my friend, whether or not there was someone else waiting, whether or not there was need to be consoled or satisfied . . . he was my friend. Some things in life you cannot ever change, and given the chance, with all the powers of a wicked and hungry mind, you do not want to change them, for as they are is the way they were meant to be.

And what happened to the list of lovers I was supposed to make when I left college? I forgot about it.

6

Man and Woman

When she met him, she had been having an affair with a married man who no longer loved her. She looked at him and thought, If you weren't such a fool, that's the kind of man you would go after for a change. She forced herself to follow him down the street. They had been drinking at the Plaza Hotel after a day of shooting the film, and all of them had been thrown out for drunkenness. He had said little. She noticed that he was tall and handsome and dressed neatly, and she knew he had recently been divorced. When the others left, for homes and wives, she followed him until he noticed her, and unable to shake her off, he invited her to dinner.

After dinner he came up to her apartment. There was no furniture in her living room because it was all sent out to the cleaners, but he seemed to think she didn't own any, and it seemed to intimidate him less. They lay on the Aubusson carpet and drank brandy. From her window they could see the lights in the park and the city. He kissed her, and she thought no one had ever kissed her like that since college; it was the only way she liked to kiss.

"You kiss so great," she said. He looked surprised.

At five o'clock in the morning he asked if he could stay over. She said no, because she couldn't sleep in a bed with anyone and they were shooting the film again the next morning. She was afraid of looking old for the camera. He said he would stay in the maid's room.

In the morning he came into her room, wearing a red bath towel, and tried to kiss her. She sent him away, pretending to be asleep. He went to the set early, before she woke up. She remembered that rejecting a man on the first date was supposed to be the way to confuse him and make him like you, but she had not planned it that way. She had only been afraid of looking old for the camera.

When she came to the set, they said good morning as if they were still only acquaintances. She made fun of the filthy shirt he was wearing and asked him if he had been out all night making love.

After the shooting was over, the young producer's wife arrived with the baby in its carriage and everyone separated into cars and cabs. He had a station wagon, and there was a girl in the front seat who apparently lived with him. She asked the girl if they could give her a lift downtown. The three of them went to his apartment, and the girl made tea while he went into the bedroom and locked the door. She realized he hated the girl. Later they were all to meet the producer and his wife and have dinner somewhere to celebrate finishing the film.

There was a parade outside in the street. They could hear the band, but they could not see it. He rushed out of the bedroom and said he was going to find the parade. She left the tea and her handbag (to reassure the girl) and followed him. He took such long strides she had to run to follow him.

When they got to Eighth Street, they found it

was only a Salvation Army parade. "I didn't know you liked parades," he said.

"I love them." She pulled him into a Howard Johnson's to buy her an ice cream cone. In the mirror over the counter she saw that he was a foot taller than she was. She looked like his child, running after a parade, eating an ice cream cone, tiny in her jeans and sneakers, and she felt like a freak. He didn't like his ice cream, so she ate both cones while they walked back to his apartment. He told her he hated the girl who was living with him and wished she would move out.

"Why don't you tell her to leave?" she said. No one had ever been afraid to tell her to leave, and she thought he was a coward.

When they came back, the girl had put Noxema all over her body, and the whole apartment smelled of it. He locked himself in the bedroom again while she made conversation with the girl and told her the parade was nice.

They all ate dinner in a Spanish restaurant: the producer and his wife, he and the girl, and she. While they were having coffee, he made three phone calls and then said he had to go uptown. She said she would share the cab, and left her coffee. She let him off at the corner of Sixty-third

Street and knew he was going to stay with a girl.

"Why don't you throw her out?" she said again, before her cab pulled away.

He called her to ask her for dinner the next night, and they began going around together. Her married lover had not called for six weeks and she knew it was over. One night they were in the Village, and she said she wanted to stay at his apartment. He said she couldn't because the girl was still there.

"Throw her out," she said.

He telephoned from the corner and told the girl to go to a hotel. It was one in the morning. They waited in his station wagon, parked by the phone booth, until they saw the girl leaving his apartment with a suitcase. She was crying and was almost hit by a car.

"She has plenty of money," he said. "She should have gone to a hotel long ago."

"Tomorrow morning I'll make French toast," she told him.

The next morning she discovered he never ate breakfast. She went through the cupboards and threw out all the health foods the girl had acquired. There were still two packed suitcases in the living room, and she used whatever of the girl's things she needed. During the night three men had telephoned asking for the girl, and he had told them to call the hotel. She did not feel sorry for the girl any more.

The next day he went to Texas to shoot backgrounds for four one-minute TV commercials and would be gone for two weeks. He wrote to her every day and sent her small presents. She wrote to him once, a long letter, saying she loved him. He wrote that it was strange he missed her so much since they had had so little time together. He hoped they would have a longer time together. She thought how practical men were.

She went to a party one night and saw a girl-friend of hers, a former hooker who had married a rich man. The husband knew and was proud he was able to afford her. The wife was so weighted down with sequins, she could not walk; she just stood in the corner while everyone danced. She was wearing a diamond ring the size of a pigeon's egg.

"Is it real?" she asked.

"Everything my wife wears is real," the husband said. He looked innocent and proud.

Schmuck, she thought.

"What happened with you and—?" the wife asked.

"It's over. I have someone new."

"That's good. I didn't want to tell you while you still liked him, but he never loved you. Everyone knew that. He was just using you for his ego. His wife knew all the time, and she didn't give a damn. She knows he has these little affairs but he'll never leave her. She knows he adores her. Why did you two break up?"

"One day I looked into his eyes and there was no one there," she said.

Her friend gasped, as if she had created an epigram. She knew it would be all over New York in a week. Just to make sure, she added, "And I don't care if you tell everybody."

"Everyone knew," her friend said. "They always asked me; they said, 'You must know, since you're her friend.' But I wouldn't tell."

I'll bet you wouldn't, she thought. "I've missed you," she said. "Let's have lunch soon."

"I hope so. You didn't return my calls, and I was very angry with you. I thought you weren't my friend any more."

She thought how much she hated this girl and

how overdressed she looked. Criticism and unkind-
ness always made her dependent and affectionate;
they reminded her of the way her mother had
treated her. She felt a rush of affection. "I'll call
you very soon." They kissed and she walked away.

That night she called him in Texas. There was
a hurricane in Louisiana, and they were cut off
three times.

"It's the FBI," he told her. "They're tapping the
line because I said I didn't like the Ku Klux Klan.
They're going to kill me."

"Don't you do a thing," she said, drunk. "I'm
coming this weekend."

The next day she bought a plane ticket and
charged it, and ordered a limousine, also charged,
to take her to the airport. She had never been to
Texas before or anywhere to meet a man, but she
knew it was what everyone did.

He met her at the airport, and she was suddenly
shy. She stayed with her luggage while he went
into the office to see if a new shipment of film had
arrived. They had fired the sound man and hired
a sound girl who was supposed to come on the
same plane she had, but there was a message that
the sound girl had gotten drunk and missed the
plane. He did not seem surprised.

"I didn't think you'd come," he told her. "Nobody ever came to see me before when I was away."

My God, she thought, here's another one like me.

The company was staying in a motel which looked exactly like its counterpart in New York. It had a free-form swimming pool surrounded by colored lights. No one ever swam in it, but people often fell into it at night when they got drunk. Texas was "dry," so they all kept bottles in their rooms and drank a lot. Her room was next to his, with its own bath, and with the door between kept open it looked like a suite.

The crew had been accustomed to coming into his room for a drink and using the room as a shortcut to get to the restaurant. The first day she threw them all out and locked the outside door. He told her they were afraid of her.

The sound girl arrived the next morning. She was very pretty, with a Sassoon haircut, chopped off on one side, and she drank vodka in the mornings. The producer seemed to feel she was his property. One night she fell into the swimming pool, fully dressed, with a glass of vodka in her hand, and climbed out, still smiling, still holding the glass (whether full of vodka or pool water it was hard to say), like a girl in an Esther Williams movie, and went right on talking and drinking.

The producer's name was Montague, and he hated her. At first she stayed in the rooms, watching daytime television and ordering room service, unwinding, feeling peaceful, while everyone was on location. The only people at the pool were a young mother with a little boy who wore a life preserver, and a Frenchman who ate alone and tried to pick her up. She cleaned the rooms, got extra pillows from the maids, and took a taxi to the shopping center, where she bought cheese and bread and tomato juice for Bloody Marys. She kept the pitcher filled with ice cubes from the ice machine in the breezeway. The room felt homey and she was happy, but he thought she must be lonesome and invited her to come on location, even though Montague was annoyed.

There were three of them in the car that morning: she, her lover, and Montague. Montague refused to speak to her. She knew he was the kind of man who would always be only a small success, live in a suburb, and hate minority groups. He was afraid of her lover, and he resented her because he had no one but the sound girl, who was always drunk, and he thought they were having a honeymoon in their rooms.

When she ran out of cigarettes, she asked Montague for one, and he pretended he could not hear her. She fought down a desire to burn the back of his neck. She asked him four times to stop at a drugstore, but he refused. Finally she stopped trying to be friendly and put on her sunglasses so he would not see her cry.

She was sitting alone in the back seat with her legs crossed and her face hidden in her collar, with the sunglasses on. Her lover reached back and drew a red heart on the sole of her sneaker.

They changed from the rented station wagon to a borrowed Thunderbird convertible so they could use a camera on a tripod. They were looking for an old house for the historical part of the film, but every time they found one, there was a television aerial on the roof. At an intersection they stopped while a dozen Negro children filed out of a bus and walked into their homes. The houses were old enough, but they all had television aerials too, so they drove on. When they finished the tripod shots, they changed back to the station wagon. A few miles later a police car stopped them and the policeman accused them of crossing the orange line.

Montague was angry and wanted to get out of the car, but her lover was driving, so he went to talk to the policeman. The policeman was a raw-faced young Texan who seemed slightly embarrassed.

"Where are you from?" he asked.

"We're shooting backgrounds for a cigarette commercial."

"You're not doing one of those integrationist films?"

"No."

"Why did you stop back there and take pictures of those colored children getting out of the bus?"

"We liked the house."

"Why did you change cars?"

"We needed a convertible to take shots with a tripod."

"Do you realize there's been a road block set up for you ever since?"

"I didn't think I crossed the orange line."

"If you want to take any integrationist pictures, you'll have to register with the office in town," the policeman said.

"We're just doing a TV commercial."

"All right. I won't give you a ticket this time. But watch the orange line."

He got back into the car, and Montague said, "I'm glad you talked to him and not me, because I would have lost my temper."

"If we were trying to get away with something, we wouldn't have driven around in a red convertible with a camera sticking out," he said. "What a fool."

She thought it would make an interesting letter to the people back home if she had anyone back home to write to.

That night Montague told her lover he thought she had better not come on location any more because she was in the way.

"Tell him I wouldn't come anyway," she said. "He makes me sick."

"Ignore him," he said, rather pleased. "What do you care if he doesn't like you?"

You like it that he doesn't like me, she thought. You like it that everyone likes you and not me. "If it weren't for being afraid you'd lose your job, I would have cut him to pieces," she said.

"Ignore him. Everyone doesn't have to like you. Lots of people don't like me, and I don't care."

"I care," she said.

She stayed around the motel and got a suntan for two days, and then the next day he said he felt sorry for her and she could come on location again because they were going with someone else. It was the writer, who hated her as much as Montague did. But the writer was a girl, so she knew she could handle her.

It was ninety-five degrees out at ten in the morning. The writer had shoulder-length curly hair and harlequin glasses and scarlet lipstick. She was about thirty-five, but she still talked about college. She did not seem too obnoxious.

"Montague doesn't want you to come on location because he says you'll alienate the natives," her lover told her. "They won't understand you."

Harlequin glasses and scarlet lipstick they'll understand, she thought. We'll see.

They had finally found the old house they wanted to shoot, gray and weatherbeaten, set back in a clearing, surrounded by pecan and chestnut trees. An old couple lived there with their two unmarried youngest children. There had been fourteen children at one time. The porch had a rocker on it, and a small Coca-Cola sign was tacked on the wall. It looked like Pop Art. She went to the edge of the porch to talk to a white cat.

"Look out, there's a hole there." It was the daughter.

"I was just going to see the cat."

"Here, kitty, kitty. Kitty, kitty."

The cat ran away. She and the girl looked at each other and smiled. "You like cats?"

"Yes," she said.

"You with them?"

"Not really. That's my boyfriend."

"That pickup you drove up in, it looks just like the truck my old boyfriend had."

The brother came around the side of the house. He was about seventeen and very handsome in a rock 'n' roll sort of way.

"Remember Henry's pickup truck?" the sister said. "The green one? Doesn't that look just like Henry's truck?"

"Sure does," he said.

"He was nice," the girl said sadly.

"You should have hung on to him," her brother said. "Ugly as you are, where you going to get another boyfriend?" He laughed.

"I got lots of boyfriends," the girl said.

They walked down the steps from the porch to watch the crew setting up the cameras. She started to hum a Roger Miller song she had been hearing all week on the radio in the room.

"What's that?" the boy asked.

"Kansas City Star."

"How does it go?"

She sang it for him, as much as she remembered.

"Do they still like the Beatles in New York?" the girl asked.

"Yes."

"And Herman's Hermits?"

"Sure."

"And do they have those funny groups . . . the Turtles?"

"I never heard of them."

"Who's the favorite?"

"The Beatles and Herman, I guess. And the Rolling Stones."

"Kansas City Star," the boy said. "I'm going to be a star some day."

"I'll bet you are," she said with real admiration.

"I'm going to git me a guitar and some cowboy clothes and go East."

"And get some rich lady, right?"

"Right," he said, grinning.

"I can believe it," she said. "We'll be hearing from you."

"My brother has a rock 'n' roll group," he said. "He plays the big towns, like Beaumont. He's there now, I think. Did you ever hear him?"

"What's the group called?"

"I don't remember." He looked puzzled. "But they're in Beaumont. And then they're going to Louisiana."

"Pretty good."

"Yeah."

"He thinks he's going to be a star," the sister said. "Ha, ha. Stupid like he is."

"Look at who's talking about stupid," the brother said. The three of them smiled at each other companionably.

"What kind of nuts are those?" she asked.

"Pecans," the girl said. "And we got black walnuts out back. My mother makes a black walnut cake. Want to see them?"

"Sure."

They went in back of the house, where the woods got thicker, and the girl and boy picked up nuts and cracked them for her with a hammer. There were pecans and black walnuts, the ones she had thought were chestnuts. She ate several and put the rest into her purse.

"Here's another," the girl kept saying. "Here's another."

"Do you go to school?"

The girl looked embarrassed. "No. I quit."

"You shouldn't do that."

"I know."

"See that hole in the porch?" the boy said. "We had a party there, with a band and all, and everybody was dancing. I was dancing with this real fat girl—Reba, remember her?" The sister nodded and laughed. "A real fat girl. So we were dancing and we fell right through the porch. We kept right on dancing, though, right there on the ground."

"They sure did," the sister said.

"What's that Coke bottle doing tied to the TV antenna?" she asked.

"I put it there myself," the boy said. "It makes the reception better."

"No kidding!"

"Yeah."

"What do you know about that!"

"Hey, tell me how that song goes again," he said.

She sang it, and then they sang it together.

The girl looked at her shyly. "Is that your husband?"

"No, it's my boyfriend."

"How old are you?"

"How old do you think?"

The girl looked her over carefully. "Seventeen."

"No. Guess again."

"Twenty-one?"

"Thirty-four."

"No!" The brother and sister stared at her. "You're kidding us."

"I swear it." She realized that the work-worn parents on the porch, who looked seventy, must be only in their fifties. "How old are you?"

"Guess," the girl said.

"Twenty-one?"

"No."

"Seventeen?"

"No. I'm twenty-four."

"You don't look it either."

The crew had finished shooting and was putting the equipment into the truck. "Here," her lover said, "hold this for me," and handed her the battery belt. It was so heavy she almost dropped it.

The girl looked at him sternly. "Where we come from," she said, "boys totes for girls."

They went up on the porch to say good-bye. "Where are you from?" the mother asked her. Here it comes, she thought; they start to hate me.

"New York City."

The woman smiled. "Well, bless your heart."

After they had driven away in the pickup truck, she realized she had forgotten to ask the two kids their names so she could send them a picture post-card from New York, and she was sorry about that.

"What did you do all that time when you dis-appeared?" the writer asked her, peering into her face with feigned amusement.

"Just looked at nuts and stuff."

"But what did you talk about?"

"Rock 'n' roll."

"Rock 'n' roll!" the writer said. "That's an area I know nothing at all about." She shook her long hair. That was a nervous habit; she was always playing with her hair because she thought it was beautiful, which it was not, but this time she was shaking her head in amazement.

And you all thought I would intimidate every-body, she thought.

That night he told her the writer had said she was glad they had let her come along because she was nicer than they had thought.

"I don't know why you care what they think of you," he added. "I only tell you these things because I know you like to hear them. They're really silly."

He had started to break out in hives that afternoon, and at first they thought some insect had bitten him in the thicket. But then the hives got worse, and he remembered that the local doctor had given him a penicillin shot the week before, before she had arrived from New York, when he had discovered he had a minor infection. She was afraid it might be a delayed penicillin reaction and gave him some antihistamine tablets she kept in her suitcase. At first he refused to take them because he was afraid of pills, but finally he gave in, but they did not do much good. The hives were mostly on his ankles and legs, and he still thought some insect had bitten him. He bought calamine lotion and alcohol, and she spent most of her time wiping up the pink mess he left on the motel-room furniture.

Now the writer said hello to her when they met in the hall. She and her lover still refused to eat any of their meals with the others, which gave her great satisfaction. One night they went into the motel dining room, which had the best food in town, and when they saw the others all dining there, they turned around and left. They drove forty miles to find a restaurant that was still open at nine o'clock, laughing all the way.

He loathed the town, the greasy food, the absence of bars, the restaurants that closed at nine at night, the movie theater that had only one showing, and the shooting schedule that made him work two days at a stretch with only four hours off to sleep and then laid him off for an entire afternoon. He preferred working all night and day to having time off, because there was nothing to do, and he wanted to get back home as fast as possible. She had been given some names of local people to telephone, but she did not want to see anyone but him. Waiting for him to return from work made her feel like a married lady. She liked it. She liked the radio playing country music and Baptist hymns, and she liked the machines all over the motel grounds which dispensed soft drinks with strange names and stranger tastes, candy, crackers, and free ice.

The ice machine was like a science fiction monster. It dispensed thousands of tiny cubes with holes in their centers, and had a door leading to its maw which you had to push down to open. He had bought three quarts of beer and had put the two they did not drink into the machine to keep cool. The next day the machine had gone insane: ice cubes poured out of the door and spilled all over the cement floor of the breezeway. He said one of the bottles must have touched a coil, and he unplugged the machine when no one was looking.

The next day the ice had melted, except for two small glaciers which she supposed contained their lost beer bottles. She put the plug back into the wall.

Since there was no place to go to eat ice cream at night, they had taken to patronizing an all-night Carnation place that sold ice cream by the quart. They would buy several quarts and some chocolate sauce, make sundaes on stolen motel plates, and put what was left over into the machine. By the next day the ice cream was always buried or stolen. Other people cached food in the ice machine too: grapefruits, melons, beer. It was always stolen or disappeared into a glacier.

One night Montague said to her, gloating, "I ate the cantaloupe you left in the ice machine. It was very good."

"It wasn't my cantaloupe," she said.

"Oh, too bad. Otherwise I wouldn't have eaten it."

After that she left bad things for him: moldy half grapefruits, rancid ice cream. She hoped he would get poisoned. The food always disappeared, so she supposed he was eating it. Montague seemed indestructible. Since she could not make him sick, she knew her project would have to be to win him over and make him like her. She wondered why it was so important that he like her.

She could not stand to have someone dislike her. In this place, so far from home, among hostile strangers, one enemy could not be ignored. An enemy had always upset her, but in a motel in Lovelace, Texas, one enemy seemed like an army. And somehow it also seemed important to keep face for her lover. He liked so much that the others respected him and resented her.

He was beginning to resent her himself.

One night he said, "I wish you would go home."

She felt as if he had hit her. Then she felt numb. "You wanted me to come here."

"I know. But I didn't know how difficult it would be. I can't work because I worry about you."

"Let me worry about myself," she said. "I just

got here, and I'm not leaving." She knew that was what other girls said. Left to her own instincts, she would have left that night. I'm not going until he does, she thought. No matter how he treats me.

One night they had dinner sent to their room and discussed love. They had steak and wine, and it was like a honeymoon. He said he felt afraid and confused. She sat on his lap.

"I know," she told him. "Emotionally we're like two high school kids necking in a car who don't know how to consummate the way they feel, so they just keep getting each other more excited and frustrated. We don't know what to do about our emotions because we've just met. But after a while we'll be calm. Time takes care of all that. A year from now we'll be able to think and feel peaceful."

"A year!" he said. "I can't stand to go on feeling this way for a whole year."

"Well, I always say a year for everything. Then if it's sooner, that's fine."

It was the best evening they had ever had. She knew he was finally glad she had come to be with him. She felt sick and dizzy with love, afraid, ready to cry, and very happy. She could not think. When she looked into his eyes, he looked dizzy and very sad. She thought he had the most beautiful face she had ever seen.

That night she had a nightmare and woke up screaming. He was frightened.

"I'm tired of being funny," she kept crying. "I want to be boring like other people. Why won't anyone let me be boring like other people? Why do I always have to be amusing?"

"You can be as boring as you want to be," he said, and kept his arms around her until she fell asleep.

One afternoon when they were in his room, the telephone rang—Montague inviting them both to have dinner with him. She was surprised when he accepted.

"You don't like him," she said.

"Well, he invited us, and we have to go."

"Dinner with the boss," she said. "How suburban." She spent an hour deciding which dress to wear. He was amused because he knew everyone else would be wearing slacks. She put on false eyelashes and perfume, and pinned on a hairpiece. She didn't want to disgrace him the way she usually did.

They went first to Montague's room for a drink.

She spilled her drink all over the front of her dress and smoked half a pack of cigarettes. Montague was being very convivial. She knew she looked pretty, even with the wet spot on her dress, and she noticed Montague looking at her with approval, or at least with desire.

There were six of them: Montague, the sound girl, the writer, a cameraman, her lover, and herself. They drove to the restaurant Montague suggested. In the parking lot outside the restaurant she found herself alone with the writer and her lover while the others were parking the cars.

"Watch out," the writer told her. "Montague is going to get you tonight."

"I thought he was being very sweet."

"That's how he's going to do it. The whole purpose of this dinner tonight is that he's going to kill you right in front of everybody."

The girl was really on her side. It was surprising how much she had changed since that day they had gone on location together. I'll work it on Montague, too, she thought, and said, "Thanks for telling me."

"Watch out," the writer said. "I really feel for you."

She felt exhilarated and smiled at the girl. "Nobody kills me," she said, feeling hatred and joy rushing through her body like strong blood.

They went into the restaurant. Montague had arranged the seating at the long table so that she was sitting opposite him. They ordered many drinks. She drank and felt high, but kept control. On one level her mind was aware that they were all watching her and Montague, listening to the two of them, waiting for the big fight. On another level she knew that she liked him, that he was generous to invite them all out to this nice place, and that she found him attractive. She was not sure whether finding Montague sexually attractive was her usual defense for dealing with men of this kind or whether she really felt that way. She did not have time to think about it.

She remembered a story she had heard that one night Montague had had a fight in a restaurant with someone and had gone at him with a broken bottle. She knew he had an uncontrollable temper. He kept goading her, trying to lose his temper at her, trying to make her angry at him; but she hardly noticed it except in a high corner of her mind that put it away where the rest of her mind could not feel it. She fawned over him. Once she

felt the pressure of her lover's toe on her foot and
knew that she had said something that angered
Montague, but she quickly turned it around so that
it became a compliment for herself and Montague,
excluding the others. She did not know what she
was doing; she went with the music of her mind
and drank the wine and looked at Montague,
thinking how attractive he was.

Really, he was not attractive at all. Nor was he
ugly. He was ordinary, a bit dashing because he
tried to be, a bit smarter than most people in some
ways, a bit stupider in others. Her mind would not
let her sort it out.

They were like tigers, caressing each other across
the table with words, looking for a soft spot to sink
in a claw, turning aside danger. She felt both excited and peaceful. She was really having a very
nice time. The others gaped at them like goldfish.

There had always been an instinct in her that
went for her own safety but skirted danger because
it was delicious. She followed that instinct now.
But there had been another instinct in her, too:
the coward's way, the way of a girl. And so now
she was planning that if nothing else worked, she
would go to bed with Montague. She was so
turned on to the instinct that she was in a state

of amnesia. She did not remember anything she or he or any of them had said as soon as it was said. She knew only the present. She felt attracted to Montague because he was cruel and did not like her, and she turned this around in her mind to mean that she was attracted to him because he and she were alike and better than the others. Her lover, sitting quietly and watchfully by her side, seemed like a child.

When the long dinner was finished, Montague announced that each of the men owed him fifteen dollars for the check. They were all shocked. She was a little surprised. This did not seem like the tiger across the table, but the old Montague, who ate spoiled melons from the ice machine because he thought she wanted them, who would not stop for cigarettes, who pretended he was deaf. He had no class, and she was disappointed. If he had planned this dinner as a killing, the least he could have done was to pick up the check so he could keep his power.

They went back to the motel. She was riding in a car with her lover and the writer, while the others drove with Montague. Her lover and the writer were ecstatic.

"You were wonderful! You were brilliant! He

kept trying to get at you and you were so clever
. . . so sweet . . ."

"What did I say?"

They did not believe she could not remember;
they thought she wanted more praise, and so they
would not tell her. I could never do it again, she
thought, because I don't know what I did.

At the motel Montague asked them all back to
his room for a nightcap.

"It's too late for us," her lover said.

"I want to go."

"What's the matter with you?" he whispered
when they were back in their room, for the wall
between his room and Montague's was thin. They
could hear laughter from the other room. "You
won. You proved your point. He likes you now.
You don't have to have a stupid drink with him. I
want to go to bed."

"I have to go," she said. "I'm not finished with
him yet. I have to finish it."

"It's finished. You won."

"Not yet," she said. What she wanted . . . she
was not quite sure what she wanted. Perhaps for
Montague to apologize for that day in the car,
although this was beyond imagining. Perhaps to
continue drinking. Perhaps not to offend him by

refusing to drink with him. Perhaps to sleep with him . . .

"I'm going alone if you won't come," she said, not unkindly. "Only five minutes. I promise. Five minutes."

He let her go. She went into Montague's room, where the other three were sitting like sycophants, perched on the edge of the bed, laughing at his jokes. Montague was lying on the bed with a glass of brandy in his hand.

"He wouldn't come," she announced. "He's a bore. Give me a brandy."

She lay on the bed beside Montague, completely at ease, slightly drunk, and watched the others as if they belonged to her and Montague now. The writer was tired and excused herself to go to her room. The sound girl was dancing alone in the center of the room with a glass of vodka in her hand. The cameraman looked as if he did not know whether to laugh or cry, but he usually looked that way; it was his nature.

Montague fetched and carried for her until the bottle of brandy was empty.

"We have a bottle in our room," she said. "Someone get some for me. I'm afraid to get it myself because he'll make me stay." She held out her empty glass, and the cameraman went to her lover's room and came back with the glass and a bottle. She knew she had been gone for over an hour, and she wondered if he was insulted and if the bottle had been his message of dismissal. She did not let herself care very much. She knew Montague was pleased that she had called her lover a bore, because he was afraid of her lover, and she knew it flattered him that she had chosen to stay.

She finished the brandy, asking Montague questions about home, his wife, and children. He spoke to her as if she were an old friend.

When the bottle was empty, she asked the cameraman to go for more, but he was afraid.

"He'll hit me," he said with admiration.

Montague went, and she felt like a tiger that had just eaten a deer. She knew how surprised her lover would be to see Montague standing on his threshold with her empty glass in his hand. That pleased her more than the fact of his going for her.

Montague returned with a bottle that had scarcely an inch of brandy in it and said it was all that was left. She drank it, knowing it was fortunate there was no more, because she was very drunk. Someone had lowered the lights, and now

Montague was dancing in the center of the room with the sound girl.

She stood up. "I guess I'd better go."

"I'll walk you to your room," Montague said.

He escorted her the five feet to the door of the next room. "I owe you an apology," he said.

"For what?"

"For that day in the car. I was very unkind to you. I didn't like you at first, but I was wrong. I like you now. I'm sorry I was unkind to you."

"You're forgiven."

He bowed his head slightly, formally, and prepared to leave. "Kiss me," she said.

Montague looked frightened. He gestured toward the door of her lover's room. "He'll . . ."

"Coward. Are you afraid of him?"

"Yes," he said, with a little smile, and retreated. "Good night. Let's have drinks together tomorrow."

She went into the room and stepped out of her dress, tangling it around her feet, and fell on the bed and passed out.

When she woke up, the bed felt strange. She put out her hand and discovered she was alone. She got up, not drunk at all or even hung over, for she never had hangovers, and looked for him. He had hung her dress neatly on a hanger, even zipped it up. She went through the open door into her own room and saw her lover sleeping in the bed, the bed they had never used. She fell on top of him and woke him up.

"What are you doing in here? Come back to bed!"

"You're drunk," he mumbled. "Go away."

She realized she was still drunk, but he was unforgivable to have deserted her. "You come back to bed," she screamed, tugging at him, hitting him.

"Stop it. I'm sick."

She hardly heard him. She kept pulling at him and striking him, dimly aware that she had broken one of her fingernails on his back. He would not get up, so she got under the covers and made love to him until he gave in and made love to her as if he hated her. He refused to kiss her.

"Kiss me."

"No," he said softly. "Kissing's special."

The next morning she discovered he had gone to sleep in the other room because she had sprawled all over his bed and he really was sick. His body was covered with swollen welts from the penicillin reaction, and he had a fever. He insisted on going to work anyway, putting on his clothes in great pain. She felt ashamed.

When he returned from location, the others insisted he go to a doctor, and Montague drove him there, exchanging a few solicitous words with her in the hall. They all felt very sorry for the invalid but thought she needed sympathy too. She was frightened.

The doctor said it was a very severe penicillin reaction and gave him a shot and some salve and runny medicine to apply with cotton. He went immediately to sleep, and she kept the others out, issuing bulletins from time to time when they came whispering to the door. The cameraman named her Nurse Jane Fuzzy-Wuzzy. She drew the curtains and sat there in a chair beside his bed, in the dark, feeling shame and sadness. She was afraid that when he awoke, he would send her away.

He woke up, finally, and asked her for a Coke. She went to the machine and brought back three. Then she put some of the runny medicine on him, although he tried to do it for himself.

"You're so kind," he kept saying sadly.

"What do you mean, kind?"

"Any other girl would be bored and leave me if I was sick like this."

"Don't be an idiot," she said.

"You're so kind."

"He apologized!" she told him. "He stood right there at the door and said he knew he was mean to me that day in the car and that he was sorry. He said he didn't like me before, but he likes me now."

"I don't know why you care," he said. "You're never going to see these people when we get home."

"I have to see them now."

"You have me."

"I'm sorry, it's just an aberration I have. Everybody has to like me."

"I hate that in you," he said.

"It's the way I am."

He went to sleep, and when he woke up, she made a cheese sandwich for him and ran across the lawn to the motel restaurant to bring him a glass of milk.

"I won," she said. "Don't you care that it makes me happy?"

"No, because it's silly."

"Well, I won."

At dinnertime Montague came by and asked if he could come in. He stood by the bed at a respectful distance, frightened of illness, and left soon. The writer told her that if she got bored, they could watch television in the writer's room.

"Why the hell does she think I want to watch television with her?" she said, reporting the conversation, but she felt pleased.

Later he felt better, and she ordered a large dinner from room service and they ate it, in good spirits. Montague came by again and said her lover was not to come to work in the morning, but that he would come by after the shooting and drive them to the doctor again.

She addressed some packages of costumes and equipment and telephoned a taxi to take them to the air terminal. After she had gotten the receipts, she took the money from his wallet to pay the driver, and then she told the writer how much it had cost, adding the cost of all the medicines, and collected the money. She felt pleased with herself because she was learning the expense account game and because she was being useful. They all seemed to think she was very clever to know how to send a package, and she realized none of them had any idea of what kind of person she was. She rather liked being thought of as a parasite, a kept woman, and stupid. It was so different from living like a man in New York.

The next day the doctor gave him another shot, but he was sicker. His ankles and feet were so swollen he had to wear bedroom slippers and could hardly walk. His hands had ballooned, and he had arthritis in his joints.

The writer came to the door. "Montague says you're both to take the next plane to New York. He's too sick to work, and we only have a day or two more shooting to do. We don't really need him. I know he'd rather be sick at home where he can see his own doctor."

"I don't think he has a doctor."

The writer wrote down the name and address of her own doctor and insisted he put it into his address book.

"We haven't heard if the equipment you sent got there or not," the writer said, worried. "I hope you did it right."

"I did just what he told me."

"I'm worried. I hope we hear. That was very expensive equipment."

"I gave you all the receipts," she said.

"I know."

He called the airlines but could not get a plane out that night. She telephoned her agent in New York, and five minutes later they had two seats on the same plane that had refused to take them. They had half an hour to pack. He left most of his clothes, which he said were torn anyway, and she left a note for Montague to bring their laundry back to New York when it was ready.

On the way to the airport the taxi stopped at the shopping center so he could fill another prescription.

"Your husband really looks sick," the driver told her.

She took care of the bags and the tickets while he sat on a bench helplessly, and then she carried their hand luggage to the plane while he leaned on her, hobbling in pain. She felt very powerful.

In the plane he said he was cold, so she got him a blanket and a pillow. He slept again and then woke when the food came, although he was too sick to eat it.

"Why did you have a penicillin shot anyway?" she asked him.

"The doctor said I had gonorrhea. I got it from you."

He was not angry, and even seemed childishly spiteful, so she realized he knew he had not gotten it from her. She knew she did not have it. Or perhaps she did. She had never had it and did not know how you could tell. If he had gotten it from her, he would have been angry. Perhaps he was making it up.

"What made him think you had it?"

"He gave me some tests. I didn't sleep with anyone but you, so I got it from you."

She wondered if she should go to a doctor in New York, but decided she was immune. Social diseases were a subject so shrouded in fear and fantasy that no one she knew ever believed he could get them. She thought of her married lover, so long ago now, and wondered if he had given it to her. If so, then he must have given it to his wife. And then it had also been true that he had been fooling around with his secretary, as someone had told her. And perhaps with other admirers.

We're all a little group, she thought. Not so little a group . . .

"You have to report diseases like that to the police," she said, knowing it would upset him.

But it did not upset him, and she knew he would not tell. He fell asleep again, and she watched over him, lovingly and all-powerful, like a mother with a child.

A MARTINI HAS AN OLIVE

But why is it that when you win you must also lose?